CROWS NEST PUBLIC
148 WILLINGDON PAR
EASTBOURNE
EAST SUSSEX
BN22 0DG

G000049352

For more information on how to order this book, visit our website:
http://www.sussexsewingmachines.com

PAPERBACK ISBN
0-9539410-2-7

First published in Great Britain in 2001

Printed by
Tansleys the Printers
Seaford
East Sussex

*First Edition*

ALL RIGHTS RESERVED

No part of this publication may be reproduced or transmitted in any form, including photocopying, recording. No part of this publication may be stored on a retrieval system or be transmitted in any form or by any means without the Copyright owner's permission.

The author asserts his moral and legal rights to be identified as the sole author of this work.

Although some events in this book are based on true incidents, the names and places have been changed beyond all recognition. I have visited many thousands of people and it would be impossible to recognise any individual from the following pages. Any similarities with any people living or dead are purely coincidental.

© ALEX I. ASKAROFF 2001

**Front Cover: Carpet Gardens, Eastbourne seafront**
**Back Cover: Seven Sisters, Birling Gap**
**Cover photographs by Sarah R. Askaroff**

# Author's Note

I must point out right at the start of this book, as I did with the last, Random Threads, Patches of Heaven, a little thing worth mentioning - although I love writing stories, as my old English teachers will attest to, I am no literary master. Be prepared for commas in the wrong place, a lack of full stops and capital letters all over the show. I thought a semicolon was part of your stomach and verbs were something to sprinkle over the Sunday roast. I sometimes try to write so much, so fast, that my fingers hurt and brain locks. My grammar on a good day is appalling, on a bad day, well don't ask. I was amused to find out that even Webster's dictionary of 1996 had over 300 spelling mistakes. This amateur production has been labour of love, not an academic triumph. Without the enthusiasm and support from so many friends, it would never have got started. Enjoy it in the same spirit that it has been written.

Why the title, Skylark Country, especially as it is not a well known bird in many parts of the world. Well, it's like this, one afternoon in high summer, Yana, Rolly (the mutt), and me, whipped up to the Downs for a quick walk in the sunshine. It was one of those perfect afternoons, a strong warm wind was blowing over the flatlands below, full of the scents of summer; the sun was still high and bright. We were walking along an ancient ridge road where travellers have walked since before records began. My book was well under way and we were idly talking about the title, we were trying to think of a name that summed up this area and how special it is. As we were talking a skylark lifted from the Downland grass, about twenty yards in front of us. The little bird hovered about ten feet above the thick summer grass and serenaded us with its beautiful full-throated song. It was right on cue, that small bird, with the voice of an angel, had told us of the title for the book. We watched in silence as it threw its song to the wind in pure joy, it summed up everything that we wanted to say and every emotion we felt, without a single word.

People ask me what I thought of my first book; I tell them that it is raw and rambling, well guess what? This book is just as bad; hang on to your false teeth, lock the door and put the answer phone on, because here we go.

# INDEX

# Acknowledgments

This is the easy part, thank you to all my friends and everyone who made this book possible. Thanks also go to Ralph who one again corrected many mistakes and to Stevie who even though she was suffering from terrible back pain, really put the book in order. I must thank Colin Bearne who used his expertise to put the finishing touches to my grammar and also Simon Francis for his cartoon and Gloria Le Maitre for her lovely watercolour of Willingford Lane. I really appreciate all of your efforts and none more so than my wife's, Yana. Yana, you put up with my ramblings, keep the kids in line and still do a thousand other jobs. You are my inspiration.

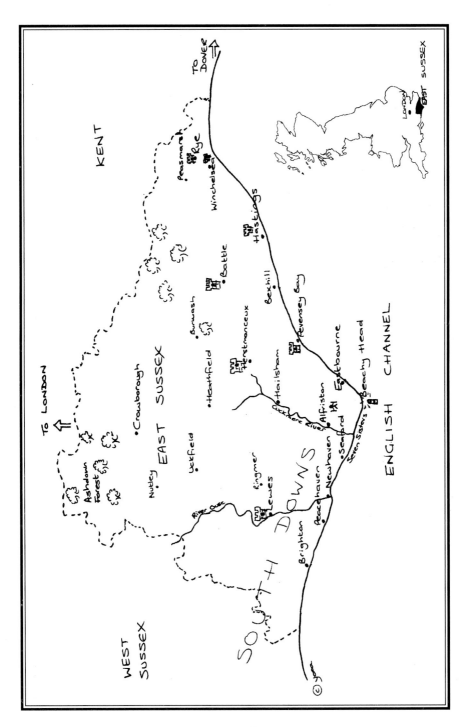

KENT

EAST SUSSEX

WEST SUSSEX

SOUTH DOWNS

ENGLISH CHANNEL

TO DOVER

TO LONDON

Rye
Peasmarsh
Winchelsea
Hastings
Battle
Burwash
Bexhill
Pevensey Bay
Herstmonceux
Heathfield
Crowborough
Hailsham
Eastbourne
Cuckmere River
Alfriston
Beachy Head
Ashdown Forest
Nutley
Uckfield
Seaford
Seven Sisters
Ringmer
Lewes
Newhaven
River Ouse
Peacehaven
Brighton

EAST SUSSEX
LONDON

© Joan

�֍ 5 ✧

# PROLOGUE

People often ask me what I see in Eastbourne and the East Sussex area and why do I write about it?

This is not hard to explain. Eastbourne and the surrounding countryside are full of memories for me. There is hardly a road that I go down or a place that I visit that does not bring back memories. The history of the area also fascinates me; I was travelling along a road in Seaford a while back and noticed a piece of iron in the corner of Croft Road. On closer examination it turned out to be a cannon. Why on earth a cannon would be supporting a flint wall is anybody's guess. On further investigation I found that there was once a great battle at Seaford and then some years later a tremendous storm. Seaford, it transpired, used to be a thriving port and had to protect its valuable shipping, quite possibly using a cannon like the one in the wall; but during the storm, the river diverted. So nature changed the course of the river, the harbour and our history. Now Newhaven, a few miles away is the thriving port and Seaford is just a little seaside town. I wonder how many people have walked past that cannon and never even seen it or wondered why there is still a huge cleft in the hills (which was once the river). People are often unaware of the interesting and wonderful things that surround them. I on the other hand believe that if I lived ten lives, I would still only scratch the surface of East Sussex, let alone the World. Though there are a million beautiful and special places on our planet, East Sussex has me gripped firmly in her spell.

One can only guess at the future, but a future without my birthplace is not one that I care to contemplate. I suppose that is much the same for many people and their hometowns, a familiarity that is comforting. Strangers that you have passed so many times, you feel that you know them; I see the pig man collecting the scraps for his pigs and the rag man that makes enough money from other peoples throw outs to run three lorries and have a house in the country. These are people that I have never spoken to but feel familiar with. I have never had the wanderlust that eats away at some; I always feel going anywhere takes me away from the place I love the most. So I am a reluctant traveller. I have always said that I would have been quite happy to be born in the olden days, knowing only where the next village was and believing the World was flat. My birthplace is my home;

luckily Eastbourne is a wonderful place. The Downs have a natural calming effect and many times when I have needed to relax, the Downlands have proved to be like a welcome friend to me. Since a child I have wandered the hills and been filled with an enthusiasm for life that is hard to explain.

Fate plays a strange hand; if the thick London smog of the early 1950s had not affected my dad's lungs so badly he never would have sought out Eastbourne with its beautiful clean air and sunny beaches. I would have grown up in the hustle and bustle of our capital instead. Could I have ever held London in the same esteem that I hold Eastbourne, even though it is one of the greatest cities on earth. I doubt it. I often drive up to Beachy Head and look down on my town. It nestles in the cup of the Downs in a large sweeping bay, with marshlands and Downland on either side. Though developers have done their utmost to destroy the area, so far they have failed miserably. Eastbourne is still one of the most charming towns on this planet. She attracts many people that feel the same way as my parents must have, when they first decided to settle here.

Being a fairly large town, of around a hundred thousand inhabitants, whose numbers fluctuate wildly depending on the season, I still expect and often do, bump into people I know. The saying 'It is a small world' really rings true here. We can only guess at the early inhabitants of the area, it is not really until Roman times that records become more obvious. Sussex was the Roman industrial heartland of Britain with great mining and iron industries. The Romans were great builders and Sussex had an abundance of something they valued most highly, chalk, which they heated to make quick lime for their concrete, add a touch of volcanic ash and they had waterproof, quick setting concrete. We know Neolithic man wandered the same area that I now roam, as did Stone Age and Bronze Age Britons. They were probably also in awe of the majestic spectacle nature had put together for us. Combine beautiful Downland and woodland with majestic rivers and open valleys. Then in more recent times, add a superbly designed Victorian town; laid out by people of vision, push the whole kit and caboodle to the seashore and you have Eastbourne, simply heaven.

This is not an idealistic view of my town, we still have our share of trouble, which comes and goes in cycles. This book is not about doom and gloom, there is enough of that being thrown in front of our faces everyday;

sometimes I avoid watching the news just to have a break from the day's tragedies. Through my life I have met people whose hearts seem as black as the inside of a coalminers sack. I avoid these people and their negative lives. On the whole, most of us have a very positive outlook on life, when disaster does strike we have an instinctive knack of coming together, getting on with life and building a better future for our children.

In reality we know the Earth has been around for at least four billion years and whatever we do to it, she will be around for some time to come. Mother nature has clothed our blue planet in the most beautiful fashion and kept it safe for us. I often stand back and admire her work. Nothing humans have ever done seems to match the natural world in all her splendour; we have never come close to creating something as beautiful and simple as dew on a petal, the smell of a new day or the smile of a child.

The following pages, much like the last book, are a rambling, rolling ride through the East Sussex countryside with its many colourful inhabitants. Come with me and share a seasonal experience from my tiny corner of the World.

*Herstminceux Castle in 2001, looking more like 1201*

*The War Memorial in the centre of Eastbourne, a proud reminder of the gallant men who fell protecting England.*

*The buttercups this year had to be seen to be believed, a memory made for a lifetime.*

*The cannon in Seaford, was it fired in anger in the past?*

# BEWARE OF THE DOG

I was woken by the radio announcing the birthday of the oldest person alive. A French woman was celebrating 115 years on our planet with some Champagne and strawberry cake. What an age to be I thought; the way my head had been pounding these last two days I would be pleased to reach the weekend.

I opened one eye cautiously and felt no pain; with a sudden surge of optimism I sat up and stared at the curtains. Yes, it had gone, the black pain that had leapt onto my neck and head at the beginning of the week had disappeared, three days of hell had gone. I saw the spring sunlight streaming in through the curtains and knew today was going to be a good day. I flung apart the curtains and opened the window. The fresh spring air engulfed me like a sweet embrace from an old friend, the breeze, full of bird song and blossom and sweet scents still held a cool trace of the recent winter.

Once dressed, I quickly swallowed a slice of toast with home-made strawberry jam, as if in joint celebration with the old French woman on her birthday, a cup of hot sweet tea followed and then straight out the door.

It was already 7.05am and I had a busy day ahead. In my mind I tried to put things into order as the Land Rover spluttered into life. I headed north, up country to my first call of the morning in the small village of Isfield. The wettest year since 1795 had left the countryside screaming for a sunny day and today it was paid in full, a glorious morning was upon us. I passed the old mare that had been put back out to pasture on common land, just before the roundabout at Halland, her dark chestnut shape shining in the early sunlight. The Black Lion Inn stood silent on the opposite side of the roundabout as the commuter traffic bundled past.

I was off to Tuckhill Farm; I had not had many calls to farms recently because of the foot & mouth disease that had plagued England for the last few months. But as it faded the calls had started to come back and I was glad of the extra work.

Foot & mouth was not all bad news, the country animals that normally get a hammering from the hunters were off the hook, no hare chasing, no fox hunting, no badger baiting, no deer culling or rabbit hunting. All these 'sports' had all been banned temporarily, whilst the countryside was off limits. This meant that the fields that were normally kept short by grazing animals were allowed to grow and show off their natural beauty; buttercups flourished like I had never seen in my life and made a memory for my old age that is normally made in childhood rather than in my fast maturing years.

As I arrived at Tuckhill Farm, their new sheep dog, Star, greeted me. She was born on Christmas Day four months ago and still full of the boundless energy that only the young have. She was all over me as I tried to disinfect my shoes in the bowl next to the straw matting that had been put down for the vehicles to roll across. Although foot & mouth was on the decline it was still important not to take any risks. Star followed me eagerly to the door, barking to let her owners know I was near. The smell of a working farm is something that is so thick, you can cut it; the silage and hay mixed with the farm animals all go to make a distinct but not unpleasant odour. Terry, the farmer was mucking out the pigs. As he saw me coming across the yard, he shouted.
'Trouble with this job, is no promotion prospects', he said, slapping the pig's bum in front of him with relish. 'You start at the bottom and never get any further because the work keeps piling up on you'. As he finished his sentence he flung another spade full of pig muck over his shoulder into a large barrow.
'Sure is a mucky job', I said with a smile and secretly thought, better him than me.

Barbara appeared out of the barn behind the farmhouse with a beautiful new-born calf in tow. She shoved the five bar gate closed with a deft movement of her bum, 'I have just given her two litres of milk and she will want another two before the day's out', she said as a greeting. The calf was busily sucking on Barbara's hand and a slimy, bubbly mess was dribbling out of the side of the calf's mouth. The calf, oblivious to this, looked to be thoroughly enjoying itself, as did Barbara.

'Damn blue tits,' Barbara cursed as we got to the back door. Leaning over to pick the milk up, she wiped some of the calf's slobber onto her trouser leg before picking up the bottles. 'They have been at the milk bottle tops again, peeling the foil off and pinching the milk', she explained matter of factly, as she kicked the back door open and threw off her wellies. I made a mental note not to have coffee; heaven only knows how much coffee I would be drinking in proportion to calf slobber and blue tit dribble.

I was shown into her living room where three machines were patiently waiting for attention. The first, an abused Toyota was hoisted onto the ironing board for work to commence. It had been worked to death. I managed to get it sewing but informed her that it may not last much longer. 'Start saving, put your pennies in the piggy bank because this one is on the way out,' I said turning to the next patient.

She knew that better than me, as she had been using it daily for 10 years. Next, the Singer 411G came up well and was soon stitching happily away. Star was upside down by my side, taking the chance of some added attention. I had to fix the machine with one hand and stroke her belly with the other.

As I stopped for a quick stretch I looked out of the patio doors across the farmland that opened up towards the distant coastline. A sparrow hawk was in full chase, and a pigeon was trying desperately to escape being its next meal. 'The female often hunts the local pigeons' Barbara said, 'They are slightly larger than the male hawks and can take down a fully grown bird'.

As Barbara finished, as if on cue, the sparrow hawk made a swirling swoop and took its prey thumping to the ground below. She then went on to despatch her breakfast with clinical precision. Soon there was a pile of feathers drifting away from the dead pigeon. We watched in silence as the scene unfolded before us, a spectacular but bloody event that was totally natural in our countryside, much as it had been forever. It was easy to see why the hawk was such a popular hunting bird amongst the ruling classes.

The last time I was at Tuckhill it was in the middle of a harsh winter. After I serviced the machine I bought a bag of potatoes from the farm. In the barn where the sacks of potatoes were loaded to the ceiling, it was as cold as ice; a chill wind echoed eerily through the open wooden slats of the barn doors. On the sacks of potatoes was a dead sparrow. The farmer picked it up and then handed it to me, it was nearly weightless, no more than feathers and skin.

'Died of starvation, poor little bugger, not even a year old', said the farmer. 'Probably came in here looking for a seed or two and perhaps a bit of shelter. It's been hard on all the wild creatures this winter', he said, looking sorrowfully at the dead creature in my hand. It is strange how some things stick in your mind. To this day I can feel that sparrow in my hand, just how mournfully light it was.

I left the family busy at the farm, loading grain into a French lorry that had just turned up from the port of Newhaven. I headed along the country lanes towards my next call at Uckfield. I arrived to find a brand new Land Rover sitting on their drive and admired it longingly as I walked past, checking out all the new seats and dials.

The customer had also just bought a new machine to replace her 20-year-old Frister & Rossmann Cub 4; she was only having the Frister serviced to sell it. I wondered if they had won the lottery but did not ask. I had to point out to her that the new machine might not compare favourably with the well-engineered Japanese Frister. She was a bit surprised as I showed her the difference inside the machines. When I left I had the feeling that the new machine would soon be up for sale, now that her Frister was running perfectly.

I was soon driving down Uckfield's busy high street and off to my next customer. I passed Tim, the flower man, busily unloading his flowers in his shop. Uckfield is always busy and gives the impression of being a friendly town. I often see people in the High Street just idly chatting. Many of my customers that live in the area have been there since childhood; there is a relaxed atmosphere and a less rushed feel to the town that I like. Before long I was once again on the twisty back roads. The early dew that had covered the fresh spring grass had disappeared and a cool wind was twisting the branches in the woods. Spring had been a long time coming this year and when it arrived it was greeted by all the creatures with enthusiasm. In the towns and villages, tulips filled the flowerbeds and ornamental cherry blossom danced above them with their pretty flowers like a thousand tiny bridesmaids playing at a spring wedding; with each gust of wind they would fly like confetti into the air. On the other hand, in the countryside, nature was putting on her own spectacular display.

The wild daffodils that had heralded in spring had started to fade into a pale yellow to be out done by the fields of rape. The glorious yellow in the fields so bright that they looked as if a child had painted a huge natural canvas in playschool yellow. The roadside verges were sprinkled with primrose and yellow celandine and in the woods, that were still bare branched, the bluebells and white wood anemone simply glowed in the morning sun. It would not be long before the forest leaves sprouted and shaded the woodlands once more with dappled light. The hawthorn and gorse bushes were in full bloom in the hedgerows. At their base, dandelions and daisies, cowslips and buttercups and many other flowers that had no name to me all nudged each other in the breeze; I drove on with a surge of energy filling a spot in my soul that yearned for this time of year. Cotton wool clouds drifted on the breeze and the whole countryside glowed; church spires picked out by the morning sun were dotted around the countryside, looking like chestnut tiled space ships pointing towards heaven.

'Time for a break' I thought as I neared the cake shop at Cross-in-Hand. The village postman was leaning against a red telephone box, chatting to the milkman. I popped into Bell's the bakers and picked the biggest jam doughnut on display. I had serviced the machine of the woman who served me some time back and we always exchange a few pleasantries. I parked the Land Rover down a sidetrack and tucked into my elevenses. As I ate, so were the sheep that were strolling around in a nearby field, examining each blade of grass as if they had never seen it before. I have an extensive knowledge of all the good cake shops in my area, while some people can name pubs, I can name the cake shops. For example, at the Pilgrims Rest in Battle, Roz makes the best lemon meringue pie I have ever tasted. Down a little side road in Eastbourne's town centre is a shop called Lincoln's Patisserie, they make some great cakes, but their jam and lemon doughnuts are to die for; and the bath buns from Windmills, the Rodmill bakery, well just the thought of them makes me weak at the knees. They are like an anti depressant, if you are in a bad mood, one bun is guaranteed to make you smile. I know, I eat like a horse, but hey, I need the energy of a horse; if I wanted to eat like a sparrow I am sure I would be nice and slim, but then I would not have the energy I need to lug around industrial machines and the like. My theory is that I need to carry at least three months extra rations on my hips. Also having my ample shape allows me to survive all sorts of natural disasters, I could get trapped in a land slide and survive for ages on nothing more than my well placed reserves. Well that's my excuse anyway and it sure is a tasty one, now I am feeling hungry again, where's that cake shop!!

Excluding the coastal towns like Eastbourne, Hastings and Brighton, the countryside around my area is mainly rural, a mixture of farm and woodland, of country lanes and dirt tracks leading to nowhere. Occasionally as you drive along, as in the Heathfield area, the woods open out with spectacular views of the distant Downland. Surrounding villages pop-up as if in a Hallmark card, a card painted on nature's canvas, but no card could ever capture the spirit of East Sussex in springtime. I call these little spots 'my patches of heaven'.

After my short break, I slipped down Hanging Birch Lane and made my way to Lions Green and my next customer. Although a lot of woods still survive in patches, the whole area was once heavily wooded and had toll roads running through the woods. Once the toll was paid at The Toll-House- like the one that still survives in Muddles Green- safe passage was allowed through the woods. However, there were other routes through the forests, concealed paths known only to seasoned travellers. The secret path through these woods was known as Dern Lane. It was the route that many travellers and pilgrims would take if they decided not to pay, or could not afford to pay the toll, it was risky. The names of the roads today reflect the way people used to think about the area, Coggers Cross, Gun Hill, Thunder's Hill, Scraper's Hill and Stalker's Lane. Dern Lane (Dern, an old translation of hidden) where my customer lived was still no more than a track up until 30 years ago.

I pulled up outside the entrance gate that stunk. It had just been heavily painted with 'creosote' wood preserver. The sign on the gate was ominous, 'BEWARE DOGS RUNNING LOOSE'. This brought back many memories of nasty brutes protecting their owner's property and also a funny incident that I once came across.

Some while back I had travelled through the ancient town of Alfriston, where the great chestnut stands in the Market Square. I was on my way to see Mrs Burgess. I had looked after her machines for years and had sold her a Babylock 750DS overlocker the year before. It was due for a service and I was going there to carry it out.

I arrived at her converted barn to find two workmen pinned to the side of her garage wall by Peg, her Doberman. I got out of my Land Rover and walked towards Peg. ' Watch out mate, she'll av' ya,' the first builder said through the side of his mouth. I knew old Peg, she was harmless, most of her teeth had been pulled and she could not run anymore.
'How long has she had you pinned to the wall'? I asked trying not to laugh. 'Nearly an hour I think', said one of the workmen. 'Every time we try and move she starts growling'. I walked up to Peg and stroked her. The builders looked on in disbelief and some disgust. 'You mean she wouldn't have bitten us', one asked in amazement.
'I doubt if she has the energy, I think she was having a laugh', I replied.

The two men muttering profanities, then got into their van and stormed off down the lane with their ladders rattling in the back. Smiling to myself, I walked up the long path to the door and rang the bell; Peg had followed me and was sitting by my side.
'Good morning Mrs Burgess', I said as she opened the door.
'Hello Alex, I was expecting someone else', she said looking past me.
'Builders by any chance'?
'Yes, how did you know? They were supposed to be here over an hour ago'.
'They were, but Peg had them pinned to your garage wall down by the gate, I don't think they will be back, they looked pretty angry'.
'Peg, you naughty girl' she scowled at her dog, wagging her finger and frowning. 'That is the second time this month you have chased workmen away'. Peg just looked lovingly at her owner as if to say, 'Hey, that's my job' and slunk off down the garden to watch for more unsuspecting visitors.
We both went in and I got to work on her machine with the faces of the two petrified workmen making me giggle like a girl.

Back at the 'creosoted' gate  in Dern Lane, I looked around; all seemed quiet so I let myself in and closed the gate behind. I drove along the twisting gravel drive to the front door and parked beside two great stone lions resting on plinths. I was greeted by the lady of the house and shown to an ailing Pfaff 91. 'It just won't work, I think the belt has broken'. My suspicions were immediately aroused, as the model 91 did not have a drive belt. ' I do hope you can resurrect her, she is a family friend,' she added. 'I sold my moped when I was 18 to buy her, I made my bridesmaids dresses on her and my daughters clothes for 20 years. So you see, she is very important to me'.

I got down to business, determined to get the beast up and running for her. Before long the machine was in parts all over her kitchen table. The problem was the motor which had dropped out of its housing and stuck in the base of the machine.

'Have you seen any screws laying around near the machine', I asked apprehensively. Hoping that they had not been sucked up the vacuum cleaner.

'Oh yes, I spotted them last week, they are upstairs, I won't be a moment'. She returned with the two special mounting screws that had normally held on the motor. 'I have had these on my dressing table for a week, I thought they must have fallen out of the Hoover'.

'Excellent, without these we would have been stuck' I chirped up, simultaneously wondering, how to get her to put the kettle on. 'It is a lovely day for a change,' I said, trying to somehow get around to a drink, the doughnut I had earlier was crying out to be washed down with some warm refreshment.

'Yes it is gorgeous outside today, not before time though, would you like a coffee'?

'I would love one, milk and two sugars please'. Ah, my simple ploy had worked, I thought. Before long we were chatting over a drink about Lions Wood. 'It is a most unusual name isn't it, do you know how it came to be named so'? I asked questioningly hoping that she had not heard the old tales of the woods.

'Yes, I have heard some local gossip, but I would love to know more, we have only recently moved to the area from Croydon, we are only just finding our way around. Mind you it is a minefield of little roads around here. The first week we moved in we went shopping in Heathfield, just up the road and then spent two hours trying to find our house again. I bet you do not meet many people that can 'lose' a house'.

'You would be surprised', I replied. 'I have been travelling around this area forever and I still get lost. Actually, it was just down the road from here that I once visited an old dear. She told me the story about Lions Wood and how it got its name; apparently it's all to do with King Richard. The story has been passed down from her family by word of mouth over the centuries. I have no idea how true it is, but the story holds water'(my way of saying that it was probably true).

While in truth King Richard was little more than a visitor to England who seldom spent much time here, and when he did it was only to raise money in taxes; he never even bothered to learn how to speak English. Surprisingly history treats King Richard kindly, I think it is because everyone loves a hero and King Richard was certainly that, he was brave, handsome and courageous and did one other final deed that is necessary for all good heroes, died in his prime, in battle.

'It all started way back in the 12th century', I said as I began my tale, about one of our most colourful kings, King Richard the Lion Heart, 'The Coeur De Lion'. King Richard was away on 'The Third Great Crusade', fighting the 'Infidel' in the Holy Land when he received word that his infamous brother, John, was up to his old tricks again. In Richard's absence, John was trying to usurp his older brother and take the Crown of England. Richard decided to postpone fighting his 'Holy War', which had ground to a halt just outside Jerusalem. He left his opponent, Saladin, in the desert, promising to return and finish him off at a later date, and pick up some of the 'new fangled' gadgets the Muslims called knives and forks.

Richard jumped aboard the first available ship, but that ended up sinking. He then decided to make the rest of the way on foot. This was fine until he reached Germany, where a greedy baron who Richard had fallen out with in The Holy Land recognised him, locked him up in a castle and held him for ransom. Eventually after bartering for his freedom, Richard with the help of his travelling minstrel called Blondel made his way to England.

Local legend has it, that they landed somewhere along the coast near Pevensey Castle, which was a favoured landing spot ever since William the Conquerors invasion in 1066. From there, with his small band of men he headed for the Capital. All the time Richard was without his personal guard he was vulnerable to attack and so he travelled incognito. He did not put it past his little brother to arrange a special welcoming home committee.

The shortest route from Pevensey to London took Richard and his men through the dangerous dense forests where wild boar and wolves roamed, also muggers and robbers abounded. They did not want to take the toll road in case he was recognised; so they travelled along the hidden forest paths. While they were travelling, night was falling; they found a clearing in the woods and set up camp for the night. After a good night's sleep and some local game, roasted on the fire, they made their way northwards to London.

In London, King Richard the Lion Heart soon sorted out his nasty younger brother and put his Kingdom back in good order. Once he had squashed John's uprising he became bored again and headed off to the continent to find someone else to fight. Unfortunately he did not last very long and died from blood poisoning from a crossbow bolt, shortly after attacking a castle in France. Ironically it was Richard who had introduced the dastardly weapon into France in the first place.

So 'The Coeur de Lion' was dead. 'Long live the King' was the cry that travelled across the land. Unfortunately the new king was going to be Richard's younger brother, treacherous King John. By all accounts, what a horrible king he turned out to be, but I am sure his mother loved him.

I retold my tale with relish and supped the last dregs out of the bottom of my coffee cup as I came to an end. 'It's a good tale, isn't it'? I asked my customer, waiting to see her expression.
'Oh yes, very good indeed, if not a little colourful' she replied with a little smile. 'Mind you that is much the same as I had heard the story go', she added. I closed up my toolbox and started to write out her receipt.

'You know Alex, if I may call you Alex, you would go down well at our local pub, they love a good yarn on a winter's night'.
I smiled and thought how true that was. I could see myself sitting by an open fire in a pub (they say the best place by the fireside was always kept for the storyteller). I could tap out my pipe on the heel of my leather boot, have another swig of ale, pull on my old grey beard and start another story. 'Maybe one day' I replied. 'I fancy the idea of that when I am old and grey'.

Meanwhile, I finished off the Pfaff, it had come up beautifully. While the owner was happily sewing away with her old friend, I packed the Land Rover with my tools. We exchanged goodbyes and I headed for the coast and home.

As I drove along, winding down the thickly wooded Dern Lane I came to Stalker's Lane. I followed it to the Old Toll-House at Muddles Green; 'Yes', I thought to myself, I could just see King Richard with his small band of men creeping through these woods, all those years ago.

*The bluebell woods near Dern Lane, a magical place in spring.*

*The perfect post office at Alfriston. The stone cross is one of the few remaining market crosses in the country. Henry IV granted Alfriston the right to hold markets in 1405.*

*Part of Alfriston High Street with the market cross and the chestnut tree planted to mark Queen Victoria's accession to the throne in 1837. Alfriston is the perfect Sussex village.*

*The village green at Alfriston. When the summer fayre is on, there will be thousands of people crammed in here. I am leaning against a floating mine used in The Second World War.*

# THE ROCKET SCIENTIST

After what seemed to be an endless winter, spring was now in full swing. It is strange that she could have gone unnoticed for so long, but she had. The foot and mouth problem had closed off the countryside to all but essential workers. Tests on the herds that were culled have shown that only a small percentage of the herds killed actually had any form of the disease, the rest were wrongly diagnosed. So this unprecedented closure of the countryside was over a few hundred animals. It seems like they have shut all the schools in the country because one child caught flu. I am simplifying it, I know, but I am sure there will be many questions asked about the handling and slaughter of so many fit and healthy animals. I am just pleased I do not have a farm; the farmers have gone through hell, only a small part of it being because of the disease itself. The good news is that the Ministry seems to have learnt their lesson and the country was slowly getting back to normal.

The rain that, a few weeks back, had fallen from the heavens for six months, decided to stop and spring was here. Yesterday the outside temperature crept to a miserable eight degrees fuelled by a bitter wind on the east coast from Siberia. But, today as I write, it is not yet afternoon and the temperature, in the shade is over twenty. The Bluebells and wild flowers that have flowered as they have done every year for centuries in our ancient land have passed with little notice this year. Mind you our British weather can change in an instant that is why we are always talking about it. We have had mornings that have started with a frost, then snow showers and hail, and by the afternoon the barbecue could be on, with thunder rumbling in the distance.

My first call of the day was to a lovely converted farm at Windmill Hill, on a ridge road, leading from the small village of Herstmonceux to Battle. The name Herstmonceux derived from the French Monceux family from the Calvados region who married into the local de-Hurst family around the 12th century, hence the birth of Herstmonceux. Herstmonceux Castle is an impressive building, set within beautiful grounds. Each year one of the largest medieval festivals in Europe is held at the castle. It is a grand affair, with falconry displays and archery, battle re-enactments, jesters and jousters, all in all, a wonderful spectacle.

The lady had an ailing Bernina Minimatic 801 with a failing foot control that only had one speed. Before long the electronics had been sorted and she was sewing happily again. As I drove out of the drive onto the main road I came face to face with the old windmill, high upon the ridge. It is a very rare windmill, built in the early Victorian period; it is on a central spindle, so that the whole windmill can turn into the breeze. It was so typical of the Victorians with their brilliant ideas, to come up with such a mill. At present it is in a sorry state, but may one day be brought back to its former glory.

My second call was to an old farmer that used to work with Jack Hargreaves. Jack had his own television show called 'Out of Town'. It came on at half past seven every Friday night and filled our living rooms with tales of old folk and how they used to work the land in times past. I loved it; even as a boy it was my favourite programme of the week.

Chapman, the old farmer, told me a tale as I fixed his leather machine that he uses to sew up his pony harnesses.

As a youngster, back before the Second World War, when the world turned at a slower pace, he fell in love with a girl from another village some seven miles away, called East Dean. East Dean lay on the other side of the Downs from Hailsham. Now, Arthur's only means of transport was an old nag called Jake. Jake was a farm horse, who had spent his life pulling the cart to Hailsham market on Thursdays and the odd trip into Eastbourne for shopping. As Jake reached twenty-two, he was put out to pasture, to end his days in peace. He would stroll around the farm that he had been born on, doing much as he liked. That was, until Arthur reached the age of sixteen and he was given Jake as a present. It was his first horse and although he had been riding him for years Jake was now all his. Even though Jake was getting on in horse years he still had a lot of life left in him. Arthur would work on the farm all day and go for rides on Jake in the evenings. Don't forget in those days, at sixteen, Arthur had already finished school a good two years.

Well, Arthur had met his true love at a Sunday cricket match on the village green; she was serving the tea and sandwiches when their eyes met.

However, there was a problem, for she lived at East Dean and he lived in Hailsham, miles away. However, now he had his own transport.

He would meet Fay at The Tiger Inn, which is in East Dean. The Tiger Inn is a splendid pub. Imagine the most perfect English pub, set in front of the village green, a little war memorial standing proud to those who had perished in the Great War. A village hall lies down a small twitten from the pub and rows of flint cottages circle the green, well that is The Tiger Inn. It is as if someone's idea of a perfect scene, like a Constable painting that has been brought to life.

To get to the pub from his home in Hailsham, he would saddle up Jake and set off around seven in the morning, every Sunday, come rain or shine. He would take a drink and an apple if they were in season. Then off he would go, along the winding lanes, past Summerhill, into Polegate, that lies at the foot of the majestic South Downs. Then he would cut up onto the lovely Downs, up into the green hills, up to the brow and along the ridge toward his true love and a good pint waiting for him at the pub. Usually within a few hours he would reach his girlfriend, who more often than not would walk up to greet him. They would spend many a happy hour talking about anything, saying nothing and yet saying everything; old Jake would wander around munching grass and lying on the soft Downland turf.

On one misty day when the hills lay hidden in a silent mist, Arthur and Fay went straight past each other. Fay, thinking that Arthur was late, kept walking towards his home at Hailsham and Arthur, thinking Fay must be sick or something, kept going all the way to her house in East Dean. There were no phones in those days so they just walked back the other way until they met up again. They had spent all day looking for each other and when they eventually did find each other it was nearly dark and time to go home again.

Normally, come lunchtime they would stroll down to The Tiger Inn and have a Ploughman's. That is the traditional lunch for a hard working farmer. Not like the stuff they dish out today. There would be a chunk of ham half the size of the plate, a slab of good old English Cheddar that had matured for a year before it had seen any daylight, strong enough to make a blind man see. Half a loaf of fresh crusty wholemeal bread, pickled onions, cabbage and cauliflower; home made chutneys, usually as potent as the beer as they were preserved with ale. Filling any spare room on the platter was a selection of fruit and veg that were in season. All this would be washed down with the local brew, as strong and rich and tasty as the meal itself. The meal would last much of the afternoon. On sunny afternoons they would chat outside on the village green, whiling away the hours as lovers do.

Before Arthur knew it, night would be upon him and he would have to set off on the long trip home. Sometimes when he had a bit too much to drink and was the worse for wear, his faithful old nag would plod the miles homeward as he slept on his back. Jake would wake Arthur at the gates of the farm by tapping his hoofs on the cobbles until he woke up.

Great days, Arthur told me, great days and happy memories. Arthur has been married to that same young girl for over half a century. After I had finished the machine, he took me to a spot at the back of the yard where the farmland began. It lay open to the Downland in the distance, on a wonderful day like this, a more pleasant a spot was hard to imagine. There was a large oak tree in one corner of the field, as Arthur leant on the fence he pointed it out to me, he showed me the small mound where old Jake rested in peace forever.

'Sometimes we have a picnic, under the tree, just me and the wife, so as we can all be together again, like we used to be, the three of us. Takes us back to those happy carefree days, when time meant no more to us than it does to the wind'.

I bid Arthur farewell and made my way to my last call of the morning. I drove away with happy thoughts of Arthur, May and Jake and their courting years strong in my mind; what great memories some people make. At my next call, a simple replacement belt on a Singer treadle 15K was needed. Within a few minutes I was all finished and the machine was clanking away as it had done since 1936 when it was made. The lady then asked if I would mind popping into her neighbour who had a bit of a problem with her machine. She would not elaborate further, but without waiting for an answer, led me by the hand like a schoolchild across the road to see her friend. I suppose to her I was about the same age as a child, still I did not mind being pulled along, my toolbox rattling as we went.

I was confronted by an old man in his eighties who had ears the size of dinner plates. His large appendages did not help his hearing as he had two huge hearing aides hanging from them like tribal African earrings.

'I cannot get the blasted thing to work,' he shouted at me as if I was a mile away. His wife came in and told him not to shout at me, at the same time the neighbour disappeared back to her home waving, happy to escape. I was left wondering what I had got myself into.

'I have spent four days trying to get the blooming thing to work', he shouted in not so high a voice as to alert his wife, who had gone back into the safety of the other room. I looked at the machine and immediately saw what was wrong.

With the man's considerable help, I went to work on the machine. I managed to move his head out of the way just enough times so that I could make the necessary adjustments. He was all over the machine, fascinated by what I was doing. At one point, the glasses that were hanging precariously on his small red nose, fell off, hitting me on the side of the head before dropping into the open top of the machine. I handed them back and like the true professional, under duress, carried on.

Once I had retimed the Italian Singer, I put it back together and made a few stitches. He grabbed the cloth in amazement and tried to run, well made the effort anyway. He went into the other room where his wife was hiding. She came back in beaming at me.
'He has had that machine for two years and it has never worked, he would not let it beat him. I am so glad that you called next door, as he would have never called you out to fix it', she said.
'Why ever not', I asked the old girl.
'Well, he was a rocket scientist and refused to believe something as simple as a sewing machine could beat him'. I started to laugh but she shook her head as he entered the room and I quickly wiped the smile off my face. He was obviously a little lacking in the humour department.

'All done now', I shouted at him as I left; he patted me on the back. I think it was a pat, I was not sure if it was a thank you gesture, or if he was just trying to push me out of his house. I left the couple, with the old man showing his wife in graphic detail what I had done. I could hear him right out on the road, he was shouting away at the top of his voice, I could see his wife nodding in an obliging fashion as if to please him and show a little interest.

'Some people never change', I thought to myself as I drove away. I felt quite happy that the Singer had beaten a rocket scientist and he had to call in a 'real expert', to fix it. Ah yes, that did make me feel good.

*The Tiger Inn at East Dean, an English pub in the perfect setting*

*Another typical country pub, The Gun at Gun Hill. Note the village notice board, post office box and telephone box. Part of rural England that has been the same since my childhood*

# THE HELPFUL HUSBAND

The beautiful spring weather of the previous few days was suddenly replaced with more heavy rain showers. Huge storm clouds rolled in from the coast carried on the turbulent south-westerly winds. The blossom that had looked so pretty only days before was being shaken and thrown from the trees. I passed a woman walking under a cherry tree; the blossom laid strewn across the floor like a pink carpet. She picked up a handful of blossom and threw it into the air; suddenly aware of her childish prank, she dropped her head and quickly walked on glancing up to see if anyone was watching her. I just smiled to myself as I went by; we are all kids inside really.

I fancy writing a poem called 'In The Shadow Of The Man', about the child that is always screaming to get away from the restraints of his grown up exterior. Maybe someday I will get around to it. Some of the kids that I see on their way to school make me laugh, the little boys about four or five always seem to be wearing these huge jackets that are way too large. All that you can see is a tiny pair of legs and a jacket walking briskly along besides their parents. I suppose like all good kids, they have been talked into having a coat that they will grow into, by parents who know if they can get away with one jacket instead of two it makes sense. We all do it.

As I drove, some of the household rubbish, which was being collected later that morning by the bin men, was blowing up the roads; the whole of my little corner of the World looked like a drowned rat. I went along the small lane to my first customer, splashing in and out of the puddles with my car; like a child in wellington boots, water spraying up over the sides of the Land Rover. Arriving at my customer, I parked on a high bit of gravel and tried to get out of the car without getting wet. If my shoes got too wet then I would have to remove them in the house and walk around in my socks. That's OK, you may think, but you have not seen the state that my socks get into.

As I walked to the door I could smell the sea, although I was a good eight miles from the coast. The strong sea breeze had brought the wild scent of seaweed and fresh salt inland to meet me. I knocked on the door and was greeted by a large black poodle nuzzling my groin in a most embarrassing way. Why do they do that?

'Hello Del Boy', I said trying to smile and push the beast out of the way as I moved past him down the hall. Mrs White was trying her best to pull the brute off me but then Rodney appeared. Rodney was another large black poodle and between the two dogs they made the simple task of carrying my tools along the hallway almost impossible. In the living room I had to stop and put my tools down for a few minutes. By playing with the dogs for a while they soon got bored. Rodney wandered out of the French doors into the wet garden; Del Boy simply slumped back down on his rug.

'What have we today then', I asked Mrs White, impatient to get started on the machine.

'Just the usual problem, Alex', She said as she uncovered the New Home zigzag machine. 'It is jammed solid, and I cannot release it, not for love or money. Even my husband had a go, but left it, moaning about having to pay you again'.

'Well it has been nearly two years and you do use it every day, so that's not too bad' I said, thinking that she was lucky the way that she sewed, to last a month out. You can tell within a few moments how people sew by the state of the machine. There are the people who have sewn for years and never build up any damage around the needle plate or hook area. Then there are customers like Mrs White who do everything from jeans to horse rugs who literally destroy their machines. There are bits of broken needles and bent pins in the base of the machine and scratch marks all over the place.

The worst machines that I always come across, are the school machines. They get physical abuse as well as sewing abuse. There is a Viscount machine at a school I know with, 'I HATE EVERYONE' scratched into the paintwork and enough stab marks from scissors to kill a wild pig. I got to work and soon had the machine sewing again.

'Now don't forget to oil it in the places I have shown you and keep it clean', I said as I left, knowing full well she would not have listened to a single word I had said. She was busily scolding Rodney who had dug up his old bone and decided to bury it in her new flowerbed, digging up her freshly planted pansies and leaving them in a mess on the path.

'That dog will be the death of me' were the last words I heard as my car jumped into life and I headed off down the road.

My next customer, Mrs Barraclough, had a strange problem. She had a newish machine, a Singer Concerto, about five years old. I started to work on the machine and once inside it found several pieces missing. 'Mrs Barraclough', I called to her in the other room. 'I seem to have come across a bit of a problem with your machine. I have found out what is wrong, but there are some parts missing'. A look of consternation came over her face and she became tight lipped. She was a large strong-built woman, not the sort to mess with.

'I told that husband of mine to keep his grubby little hands off my machine' she almost spat out of her mouth.

'Is there somewhere he might have left the bits'? I asked hoping to calm her down a bit.

'I shall have a look in his tool box', she replied walking off at a fast pace towards the garage. She came back in, red faced, with the box. 'Is there anything that you recognise in here,' she said, pushing the box towards me. I looked through all his tools and bits and pieces, but the parts I needed were not there. Normally I carry loads of spares but only for parts that might wear out, but not parts that have been pinched by tampering husbands.

'Can't see anything, I am afraid', I said in a placating manner in the hope not to annoy her further. 'Anywhere else he might have put them'? I said, raising my eyebrows in a positive manner as if to encourage her mind to leap to my assistance.

'I just can't understand it, he never touched it while I was here, he would not dare', she fumed, pulling out drawers in a side cabinet.

'What does your husband do', I asked enquiringly?

'He is an electronics engineer, but, I am sorry to say, he will have a go at anything. Last year he blew the washing machine up after shorting out the pump motor and the year before that he nearly killed me trying to service the microwave. Is there anyway you can fix the machine without the parts'? she asked.

'I could take it with me and order the pieces; they are quite small but unique to this model'.

'One moment, I have an idea' she beamed at me. She phoned her husband at work. 'Could you put me through to Martin, it is Marjorie, his wife' She said to the receptionist. There was a silence for about a minute before I heard her say, 'Don't you hello darling me, I have the sewing machine engineer here, fixing my machine, is there anything that you would like to tell me about the sewing machine'?

'Blimey' I thought, I could see who wears the pants in this family. I could just feel the poor husband squirming on the other end of the line.

'Well, if you have not touched the machine, how come there are three parts missing from the inside that could not possibly have fallen out of the machine on their own'? Another silence; 'look it is quite simple Martin, tell me where the parts might be or I am coming down to the factory right now and pulling you home by your ear, I am sure your colleagues will enjoy that'. I could hear an apologetic whine emanating down the phone line. 'That's better Martin, now go back to work and make sure you bring some flowers home with you, that is if you want to eat tonight'. She put the phone down and turned to me with a triumphant smile, like a cat that has just swallowed a mouse.

'They are in his dressing gown pocket. He came down one night last week while I was asleep and tried to fix it. After trying for two-and-a-half hours he finally put it all back together but had three pieces left over and hoped that you would not notice them missing. I am very sorry about this but he is always up to no good', She said marching off to the bedroom. She returned moments later holding three sewing machine parts in her outstretched hand. 'I believe these are what you are looking for'? She said handing me the items. ' I think tonight I am going to prepare Martin a nice hot curry, yes a very hot curry indeed'.

Before long all the parts had gone back into the machine and it was sewing as well as the Concertos will ever sew. Which was just as well for I dare not think of my punishment had I failed to correct the machine! I packed my toolbox up and called Mrs Barraclough in from the kitchen where a strong smell of curry was starting to fill the air. 'All done', I said, 'she is sewing like new'.

'Good, well done. This afternoon I am starting on my new bedroom curtains'.

'Supper smell's nice', I said, almost laughing, the smell alone was starting to make my eyes water.

'Oh, Martin does like a good hot curry' She smiled as she answered back. As I left the house she was busily stirring in more curry powder into her husband's supper, 'poor bugger', I thought, what a woman to be married to, I would not want to cross her path on a dark night.

I loaded the Land Rover and hit the road, laughing at the thought of her husband's face as he took his first mouthful of curry. Mind you, that will teach him not to mess with my machines.

I knew I was in for trouble with my next customer right from the start. The phone rang and my wife answered it. An old dear started to enquire how much it would cost to service her machine. She seemed quite scatty and I could hear my wife repeating almost everything twice; she persevered on. When it came to part of her address, my wife started to snigger. Then repeated to her, 'I see so you live in the house next to Betty do you, and where does Betty live'? There was a few moments silence and then my wife said, 'Oh I see, so Betty lives next door to you'.

I spat my coffee over the computer screen. The silly old woman had thought that would be enough information for me to find her house. I crept to the phone with my wife still trying to find out where the old lady lived. To stop myself from laughing out loud I wrote on a pad, 'just tell her to light a flare at the right time, I will keep an eye out for it'. By now we were both having trouble trying to control ourselves and the old dear had gone to pieces. I went off to get a cloth to clean up the mess I had made. Eventually enough details were dragged out of the old girl to arrange a call the following week.

At her house, I knocked on the door and saw a shadow of a figure slowly making its way to the door. 'Who's there', came a voice.
'Its Alex, I have come to fix your sewing machine'.
'Alex', she said enquiringly.
'Yes, Alex, do you remember, you booked an appointment with me to have your sewing machine serviced'? I put more emphasis on the words to jog her memory.
'How do I know it is really you'? What on earth do you say to that, I thought.
'If you open the door you will be able to see that it is really me', I said thinking I shall have to outwit her somehow. Now, she has never met me before so seeing me would be of no use, but I thought the ploy might be

worth a try.

'Do you think I am stupid'? came the reply. Well, now what do I do? I had a brainwave. 'Listen Mrs Jackson, I will get the office to give you a ring so you will know it is me'.

'That will be fine', came the reply. I whipped around the corner and rang her on my mobile; I had all her details as with all my calls for the day, on a sheet in my folder. The phone rang, I could hear it ringing in her house. 'Hello, Mrs Jackson, our engineer will be calling on you any minute now. His name is Alex, and he is going to fix your sewing machine, so make sure you let him in or he will not be able to mend it'. I hung up and ran back around the corner to my toolbox that was by her front door and rang the bell.

'Who is it', came the same old reply.

'It is Alex, to fix your machine,' I shouted through the letterbox.

The door slowly opened and a tiny old girl looked up at me. 'You are very quick young man, I only just made the appointment a minute ago'.

'I like to be punctual Mrs Jackson', I replied trying to keep a straight face. I followed her at a snail's pace along to the machine which was on the floor in pieces.

'What's happened to this then'? I said, bending down to examine the machine.

'I think it needs a good service', she replied staring at the mess on the floor. 'It may need a service,' I said, 'but not from me I am afraid, you could try a priest. There is nothing I can do to resurrect this machine it is smashed to bits'. I picked all the pieces up and put them together on the table for her, heaven knows how long it had been lying on the floor. Before leaving I made the old dear a cup of tea. 'How is Betty'? I asked enquiringly, making conversation over our tea.

'Betty, Betty, she died years ago' she mumbled. I nearly spurted out a mouthful of tea. That's twice she had done that to me. I decided to change the conversation and went back to the machine. Unfortunately that got me nowhere, 'I am going to sell it', she said as I left, 'I have hardly used it you know' she added, all bright eyed and cheerful. I just shook my head in despair, thinking of all the trouble she will have. 'Well good luck to you then' I replied as I hit the road, realising the futility of trying to explain further.

Some people, I thought. Mind you she will probably live to be a hundred and cause chaos everywhere she goes. I might not have been paid for my call but she did give me a laugh, and sometimes that is worth much more than money.

*The Coach House in the 'Old Town' part of Eastbourne right next to St. Mary's Church. This is where many a weary traveller would have rested on their pilgrimage*

*Beachy Head with sweeping views across the Downs and Brighton, no more than a speck, in the far distance*

# MARVELLOUS MAY

There is no doubt, that the most wonderful month of the year in Southern England is May. The whole countryside comes to life in a display that no part of our World can improve upon. On sunny May days your soul fills up with the sights that surround you, even if you are not aware of it. I have noticed over the years that most people are in an upbeat mood during this month. People are more friendly, approachable and pleasant. Research has just shown how we react to the colour green in such a positive way. Hospital patients that are moved near a window recover nearly twice as quickly as those that are not and need fewer painkillers. Green is the ancient Egyptians' colour of rebirth in the afterlife; in spring; it does really feel like a new year is here. You can walk past a person every month of the year, but in May there is more chance a stranger will say 'Good Morning' to you than any other month. Mind you it is not always the case, as with my first call of the day.

As I rang the doorbell of my customer, two dogs started to howl. It was not the normal barking of inquisitive animals but the trained bark of animals that want to see the colour of your blood. I looked around and judged how far I would need to run if they came at me; I was about 10 yards from the Land Rover. I knew I could make that in a few seconds. It is funny what skills you learn in my business, I would make a great burglar. I have learnt to tell from the noise of a dog if it is friendly, lonely or on heat, or even if the owners are out. If a dog is left in a home on it's own, when I knock on the door it barks, but at the end of the bark there is always a short whimper. This signal lets me know that the owner is out. It is always annoying when I hear that little extra at the end of the bark because it means some silly sod has gone out and left me standing at their front door.

I have only been bitten a few times in all the thousands of house calls I have made, so I must have a positive effect on most animals. In fact, I have surprised several owners when I have not been attacked. More than once they have cross examined me as to why the dog had not barked or attacked me, I suppose I never seem to be a threat to them or their owners.

Back at the house I heard the dogs being locked up and breathed a quiet sigh of relief. Shortly after, a quite unpleasant man in a light blue shirt pulled the door open. 'Good morning, I have come to service the sewing machine,' I said with my usual smile. I was greeted with a blank stare.

'Come in' he said in a short manner.

'Charming' I thought, the spring weather has done nothing to put this guy in a good mood. He led me to the machine, a Janome Mystyle 22. A smashing little machine, which embodies most of what is good in a modern machine. I set about the machine, the motor bearing had seized and needed to be stripped out and released. A local shop had quoted them such a high price that they had decided to buy a new model. I persuaded the owner to let me have a look at it first to see if it I could repair it; within half an hour the motor was out, stripped and the bushes released. No offer of a drink, no polite conversation just a dry stare whenever they went through the room. Probably checking to see if I was pinching the silver and sneakily rolling it into rags and hiding it in my toolbox.

It is one of the many things I have noticed, how we can instantly like and dislike people. Rather like dogs in that respect. Why? Well who knows, but someone can open a door and in a split second you can feel uneasy and can't wait to finish the job and get 'the hell' out of there. In other houses you would be happy to bring the wife and kids and stay for week. Anyway at this house I was happy to hit the road to my next customer. He would have said 'Thank you', but I think it might have choked him. Still you can't have everyone happy all the time; what is it they say, 'It takes a little rain to make a rainbow'. As I left, the husband released the dogs that instantly ran towards the gates howling as hard as their lungs would let them.

I was off to an old customer of mine in Brightling, just a stone's throw away from yet another one of my favourite small villages, Burwash. The road from Heathfield to Burwash is High Weald Country. Superb views lay on both sides of the ridge road that I have renamed Paradise Drive. I always drive along the road slowly, which to many of the travellers in a rush is annoying, they do not realise what they are missing. The views are so rich, so appealing that you could bottle them and sell them to old people to make them smile. As the road leaves Heathfield you can see rolling farmland and forests sweeping away into the distance. Oast houses and farmhouses dot the green landscape and the eye travels easily through East Sussex into Kent. Oh, to be a bird to soar over such a rich landscape, to swoop and dive in the sweet Spring thermals that smell of wild honeysuckle and fresh meadow grass. Buttercups fill the fields with tiny spots of sunshine and rhododendrons splash out their colours to all that want to see. I do love May in my little corner of the World.

May is also like a new dawn over the countryside, the trees that have been doing a good impression of being dead all winter have sprouted into vibrant greens, even the lazy English Oak that always over-sleeps like a teenager on a school day has awoken; they spread their rich green foliage over the cornfields to let you know they have come back to life for another season. Time means little to such a tree. What is a hundred years? It takes that long just to reach a decent size. An oak can laugh at us simple humans as we pass through their slow secret world. We are lucky to see 70 spring-times, 70 seasons, 70 blooming of daffodils; 'Three score year and ten'.

I had learnt when I worked all the hours in the day at the old family firm, Simplantex, that time is a deceiver, slipping by you most days almost unnoticed. I think that time is just there, time is eternal; it is humans that have put hours together and made 24hrs into a day. The cycle of life and weeks and months all belong to a far deeper-rooted cycle of space and time; of light and dark and rotations of the moon, but in reality they are not measurements of time. The awful truth is that although we try and limit time to years, decades and millennia, time does not disappear. It is us that disappear.

This revelation presented itself to me in my late teens and gave me a constant urgency; to do everything with my life that I possibly can, for as long as I can. I am a terrible fidget. I can't sit still for very long before I get 'ants in my pants' and have to do something. I am going to make an awful old man someday. There is an old Sussex saying that I love and sums it up perfectly, 'eat well, keep fit, die anyway'.

As with this new spring, the new vibrancy of the colours in the countryside will soon disappear into more dull and dusty greens; but for now the rebirth of the countryside is in full swing and it is impossible not to be affected by it. Every blade of grass, every leaf that catches the morning sun shouts its glory.

Many fayres are held at this time of year and the Laughton Fayre is held on the Whitsun Bank Holiday, as is the Battle Medieval Fayre. I had recently called on a customer who was making all the archers' costumes for the

Battle Fayre. It was a heavy deep red cloth that was made exactly as it had been, in the 12th century; it looked great, but what a 'pig' to sew. They have re-enactments outside the Abbey walls of the great battle between Harold and William. It was a winner takes all battle and as William won, the Normans took England for centuries. Outside the Pilgrims Rest they roast a suckling pig with jesters and jugglers entertaining the crowd. You have to put up with the Maypole dancers but, although we always think they must be barmy, we all love watching them dancing around the Maypole. Maybe we just don't believe anyone would really want to make a fool of themselves that badly; but, all said and done, it is good clean family fun.

I passed the busy Heathfied Market, which is held every Tuesday on the outskirts of the small town, and headed off towards Burwash and Brightling. One of the roads to Batemans, Rudyard Kipling's home was closed due to foot and mouth; so I had to take a small detour through Burwash. Past the well trimmed beech trees that form a column on either side of the High Street, past the Old Forge and pub, along to the War Memorial and church. Then I slipped down School Lane and made my way to my next customer who lived in a peaceful spot in the middle of nowhere.

I have called on Rose many times over the years, she has a small cottage down a quiet lane where you can hear the skylark and song thrush sing; is called Wisteria Cottage. In May the whole front of the cottage is dripping with lilac fronds of wisteria, it hangs above the porch like bunches of lilac grapes, and looks stunning. Rose always has the wisteria trimmed twice a year, 'that is the secret of making your wisteria bloom', she once told me.

Today was a bit different to my normal calls. I pulled up along side a builder's lorry, 'what have we here then', I thought. The usual songbirds were replaced with the grinding of a cement mixer. Two dirty looking sheep dogs ran up to greet me as I entered the gate. I was a bit worried by them as they started to stalk me. They did not bark but one shot around behind my back while the other dropped to its stomach in front of me. I decided not to move for a while to try and see if they were friendly. However, each time I took my eyes off one it would creep forward, so I kept trying to swing around front to back. This was a game that they were far better at than me and within a few seconds they were right on me.

'Patch, Blackie, down', came a perfectly timed voice from around the corner of the cottage. A large builder stripped to the waist with an ample belly hanging over a pair of blue jeans summoned the dogs away. 'They are alright mate, once you are in', he shouted over the noise of the mixer and waved me forward.

I went to the front door of the cottage that was normally framed in beautiful wisteria; but today it looked very drab and distinctly unloved. I banged loudly on the door and waited, then banged again. I then walked around to the side of the house where the builders were busy doing things that builders do. 'Anyone in', I shouted to the three men.
'Should be,' shouted one of the men back, 'Try round the back'.
I went around to the conservatory on the back of the cottage and spied Rose in the conservatory busy lighting up a cigarette. I waved to her but she did not see me.

'Hello Rose', I said as I got to the open conservatory door, she leapt up, knocking the ashtray off the table.
'Oh you gave me a shock', she said picking up the ashtray. 'Come in Alex, the machine is under the table. You will have to forgive me I am a nervous wreck, the builders have been here a week and it seems like a year'.
'What are they up to then'? I asked enquiringly.
'They are building a breakfast room, but we have run into so many problems already that it is driving me insane. I only moved to this spot because it was so peaceful and now it is like living on a motorway in the rush hour, and their bloody dogs, scare me to death, each time I go out of the door they hunt me like a wild deer. The worrying thing is they never bark.'
'Never mind, it will all be over one day', I said positively.
'Yes, I suppose you are right. It just seems to be endless. That's not the half of it either' She went on. 'I have my son and his wife upstairs with their new baby. The cats won't go outside because of the builders dogs so they are messing all over the place and to top it all they have broken the water mains this morning'.
'Time for the Valium I reckon then', I said with a smile. 'These things are sent to try us, still, think how nice it will be when it is all done'.

I settled down to work and soon had her old New Home sewing machine purring along. Mind you it sounded quiet because of all the other noise going on. The baby had started to scream and the bulldozer was moving some ballast around to the side of the building. I left Rose looking bedraggled and worn at the back door. 'I won't see you out, those dogs will have me', were the last words she said as she lit up another Rothmans.

I was glad to get away from the noise, but no water meant coffee was off the menu, which was bad news. Anyway, I was off to Ron and Janet's at Ninfield, they were always good for a drink. I made my way down the old back roads from Brightling to Dallington and then Ponts Green and Herstmonceux, before turning down the Ninfield Road. What a pleasure, the drive was through the Sussex country lanes, no traffic, just the odd tractor and horse. The gorse in the hedgerows this time of year is simply spectacular, it is known locally as 'Firecracker' because of the sound it makes when it shoots out its seeds on hot summer days. The bushes look like exploding fireworks that have been frozen in time, their long, green, slender shoots with yellow flowers bursting out along them, capture the very exuberance of May. Before long I arrived at Windymead in Pottmans Lane and opened the gate to Ron's drive. Outside was a small table of runner bean plants and tomato plants; hardened off ready for planting. There was a jam jar to put the money in and a note pinned to the table, 'ALL PRODUCE 50P'. I made a note to check out his other goodies in the back garden.

Ron and Janet are both locals, born and bred. Janet came from the Pont's of Ponts Green and Ron from a long line of country folk. They have been married for over half a century and yet were born in the same road in Herstmonceux. Ron was born in Rocks Cottage along Victoria Road and a few doors down, Janet had come into the world. Janet is several years older than Ron so although Ron is in his seventies he is still referred to as 'THE TOY BOY'. Ron was busy in the back garden planting seeds in his garden-come-allotment. Janet was sewing away making pinnies (aprons) on her Frister & Rossmann.
'What's up today then'? I asked Janet as I walked into the living room and gave their overweight Labrador a stroke.
'The old girl just went bang' Janet replied, pointing at the Necchi in the corner. 'It gave me a right shock, I would not let Ron have a go; you know how he likes to fiddle'.
I remembered well the last visit, Ron had put the Necchi foot control wires in the wrong way round and left two live prongs sticking out. 'Just as well

Ron's not been at it', I said, 'It should not take too long'.

At that moment Ron appeared from the back door with a big smile, 'Morning Alec' he said in his thick Sussex accent, touching his peeked cap that seemed to be permanently fitted on his head. Ron never could say Alex, so to him I was Alec, and that was fine by me. I set to work on the old Necchi as Janet kept sewing away on her Frister & Rossmann. She had bought the F&R to replace the Necchi but had carried on using the old machine as long as she could, much preferring the smoothness of the Italian machine.

While I re-soldered the wires in the back of the motor, Ron was busy telling me tales of the old days back in Herstmonceux; of how he would work all week as a kid to get enough money for a beer, a pack of cigarettes and the price of a ticket to the Herstmonceux Cinema. After I finished the machine Janet packed the F&R away and pulled her old favourite in front of her. 'Ah, my old friend' she said as she stroked the top of the Necchi. I sat with Ron and drank my coffee as he went back to tales of the old country, in times long past.

We 'settled up' for my work, two pinnies newly made; one short pinnie, powder blue with yellow leaves and the other a turquoise long pinnie with fish and crabs all over it and a box of pansies for my flowerbed. Before long I was heading away from Windymead with Ron waving from the gate, down to Pear Tree Lane and the marsh road.

As I pulled along the marsh road I could see the outline of the South Downs calling to me in the distance, the large willows that line the way were swaying in the fresh spring breeze, their long slender leaves flowing with the wind and catching the sun like weed in a stream. I could see the dip in the hills known as the Saddle, my house lies at the foot of that part of the hills, so wherever I am in East Sussex I know exactly where home is.

It had been a long morning and a lot of miles travelled, but in May I would gladly pay to travel them every day.

*Maypole dancers that always draw a crowd with the great Battle Abbey behind. We enjoy watching them as much as they do dancing. The maypole dance was an old ritual to make the soil fertile for the crops, it dates back to pagan times.*

*The Cuckmere vale - the flat lands below the Down's - a timeless scene*

*Little Laura and her dad, Dave at the Laughton Fayre. My god-daughter enjoyed every second of the fayre, mind you so would I, if I was pushed around in a comfy chair*

*The bright yellow fields of mustard and rape are a splash of colour over the downland. This is refreshing, just like a childs painting - even in black and white picture it is superb.*

Summer arrived late this year; experts say it has been the wettest May since records began. It certainly felt like it.

## <u>SKYLARK</u>

*Now is not the time for words to be spoken,*
*It is a time for feelings to be felt.*
*I lay beneath a giant oak*
*Gazing skyward through her fresh summer leaves,*
*She is wearing the blue sky like a silken scarf,*
*And looks as pretty as a Spring bride.*
*Her branches sway softly in the warm afternoon sun,*
*While shimmering shadows, fall over my contented face.*
*The recent rain has made the Earth smell as only it can.*
*Hawthorn blossom leaves a heavy musk in the air.*
*A squirrel chases his mate,*
*She skips on an invisible path through the trees.*
*All is as it should be.*
*And at last, the Skylark sings.*

*Alex I. Askaroff*

# ENA, WILF AND THE ONE-ARMED MACHINIST

Back in the 1940's and 50's there was a live radio broadcast from the BBC. A radio announcer pronounced in his perfect RADA trained British accent, 'BRITISH BROADCASTING LIGHT AIR ENTERTAINMENT PROUDLY PRESENTS THE WILFRED PICKLES HOUR'.

The weekly, evening show was run by Wilfred Pickles, and his long-suffering wife Mabel; with Ena Sharples from Coronation Street, playing the piano. On a Tuesday evening the nation sat glued to their radios while Ena would fill their homes with her energetic piano playing, or rather 'tickling the ivories' as Wilf would say. One of Wilfred's show features was to ask any listener if they had a good yarn to tell. The listener would call into the program and if the story sounded interesting enough, Wilf and the team would hotfoot it down to the person and do a live broadcast from their house in the following week's show.

Well, on one occasion my customer Mrs Holly phoned the BBC and told them about her neighbour, Mrs Connolly. She was a lady who had lost her husband in a fishing tragedy. Mrs Connolly lived in Grimsby the fishing capital of England and after her husband's untimely death, managed to bring up her four children all on her own. What made the story even more amazing was this woman not only brought up four well mannered and well behaved boys; during the worst years of the war, and the austere times after it, but she did it with only one arm.

Wilf and his team turned up for their live broadcast, set all the equipment up in Mrs Connolly's living room and started their show. Wilf would begin his evening entertainment with a quiz and when someone won he would shout out to his wife in his thick Yorkshire accent, 'GIVE EM' MONEY MABEL', Mabel would duly hand out the prize money and on went the show.

When the time came to talk about the week's story, Mrs Connolly started chatting to Wilf about how she made ends meet and how the Seaman's Mission had been such a great help with support and an extra bit of income. She then went on to say that she made all her own clothes on her wonderful old Singer sewing machine. Now this was live 'on air' and you were not allowed to mention any specific names of products. There were strict regulations regarding advertising on the radio; but the name Singer had just popped out, too late to do anything about it now, a nation had heard. Wilf stuttered a bit and carried on with the show hoping no one had noticed; how wrong he was.

The effect was electric and Singer shops all over the country were bombarded with calls for their machines. Singer's top salesman was quoted as saying they had their best month's sales since the 1930's. At their Head Office, Singer they came up with a devious plan to milk the effect that the good lady Mrs Connolly had on their sales. They decided to treat her to a brand new Singer. They arrived, a month later, on her doorstep with photographers and reporters on hand, to a carefully staged 'surprise'.

Mrs Connolly dressed in her pinnie and a scarf covering her hair opened the door. She stepped back a little in surprise as the Singer sales manager started with his loud advertising 'dribble'. 'We are here today', he stated, 'to donate this beautiful new Singer model 99 to you, Mrs Connolly, for your courage in the face of hardship. We do hope that you will get as much use out of this superb model as you have had faithful service from your good old reliable Singer machine in the past'. Mrs Connolly looked on in bemusement as the cameras clicked and flashed away and reporters busily jotted down what the sales manager had said. Silence fell as they waited for Mrs Connolly's warm response to such a gift. Mrs Connolly was supposed to be flushed with enthusiasm and wonder at her marvellous gift from the great Singer firm.
'How in God's name am I supposed to use that, you daft hap'orth', it is a hand machine and as you may be aware, I have only got one arm', she said waving it at him like he had never seen an arm before.

The crowd erupted into laughter. Singer's had failed to note that her old machine was a treadle, which she could comfortably use with one arm.

The reporters started to heckle and more flashes popped away at the red faced Singer head office manager, but in true Yorkshire tradition, Mrs Connolly had not finished. She was not going to let a gift slip away, even if she could not use it.

'It'll make a nice Christmas present for my new daughter-in-law, bring it in and put it on' table, now what else have you brought for me'? She demanded, pulling him past her into the house. She turned to the small crowd of onlookers.

'Now clear off the lot of you, before I call the police', she shouted to the crowd and waved them away with her hand.

Well, that was the last they saw of the Singer man from Head Office, he crept out the back way sometime later and was unavailable for comment for the next few days. Everyone had a good laugh at Singer's expense, including Wilfred who added a few gags into his show the week after the incident. As for Mrs Connolly, well she just kept on sewing with her good old treadle.

*A mediaeval battle re-enactment, these events take place all over the country at different times throughout the year. They draw big crowds and if the weather is fine is great entertainment.*

# SATURDAY BY THE SEA

'Ah, another Saturday', I thought as I started my weekly stroll with Rolly along the Eastbourne promenade. Seven o'clock in the morning, and hardly a soul insight. The council cleaners were busy clearing up after the nightclubs that had closed a few hours earlier. What a day, early summer, no wind, the sea looking like a milky pond fading away into the horizon; it could have been drawn on a draughtsman's board only interrupted by the gentle slopes of Hastings nuzzled into the distant coastline like sleeping lion's feet. In the quiet of the morning, the gentle lapping of the waves on the shingle was sweet music to my ears; you always feel a little closer to heaven on days like this. It had been another busy week but they always are nowadays. It was just a memory now. The days when I would wait eagerly for the phone to ring and hope it was work, any work, from sharpening scissors to fixing sewing machines; how desperate I was for employment in the early days of my business; and keen, boy was I keen. I would chase any call like a double- glazing man would chase a lottery winner.

Rolly, my dog, was engrossed with the smells on the pavement, as all dogs seem to be. Why they are so fascinated in these scents is beyond me, and probably just as well. The low sun was reflecting off the flat sea as the occasional small wave rolled lazily onto the shore. It was throwing up dazzling lights like camera flashes at a concert. In the distance on the horizon the outline of the Sovereign Lighthouse looked like a giant cross summoning passing ships. There is something so special about early mornings. As children, my dad would often drop us off for a spot of night fishing on the beach. I would stay up all night besides a roaring fire made from driftwood, with potatoes baking in the ashes. How wonderful it was to watch the moon make silver paths across the sea and the clouds play hide-and-seek with the stars. When dawn approached it would start to get light but it would go dark again for another half-an-hour before the real dawn started; this was the pre-dawn. As the sun moved towards the horizon, we would be waiting and watching, mesmerised by the changing colours of a new day and the sign that our adventure was coming to and end. Dad would turn up with hot coffee and doughnuts; we would pack up all the gear and on the odd occasion some fish, go home to sleep blissfully, dreaming of our night-time adventure.

Still smiling at what the tramp had said, I passed by Eastbourne's superb Victorian pier; the old lady who feeds the pigeons was throwing the contents of her bag of titbits into the air, the pigeons flocking around her, some doing good impressions of Max Wall, (an old British comedian), as they nodded along the pebbles. The starlings that roost in thousands on the iron rafters under the pier had already left for their feeding grounds around the parks and gardens of Eastbourne. They provide such a brilliant attraction doing aerial acrobatics each evening looking like shoals of air-born fish that sweep in waves over the pier in perfect harmony as they do a ritual air dance. After a few minutes acrobatics they come into roost for the night. Starlings, like many birds have 360 degrees vision, this allows them to know exactly where each other bird is and thus avoid colliding. The only slight down side to watching their wonderful antics is that you often get an unwanted splattering of something nasty.

The charming and picturesque Chatsworth Hotel was busy setting breakfast tables and getting ready for the morning rush. An enticing smell of bacon and eggs drifted across from the hotel, which made me crave for a good 'fry-up'. The 7th Duke of Devonshire looked solemn, sitting, gazing out to sea between the Mansion and Cavendish Hotels where he sits immortalized in bronze for eternity. Mind you he did not have much to smile about, the local seagulls had given him a white cap of droppings that looked like one of the holiday-maker's handkerchiefs that they tie around their heads to protect them from the sun. I remembered how heavy the newspapers were that I delivered daily to the hotels when I was a boy. I would have around 40 or more papers balanced precariously on my bike rack as I made my deliveries to each hotel. There were always the extra papers needed as well, for a late guest who wanted his Telegraph or Times. So one trip would be slow and tricky then I would bolt back to the hotel like a young rabbit, with the extra paper tucked under my arm.

Suddenly a tramp appeared out of a shelter, a half empty bottle of beer in his hand, 'Morning, monster' he said to Rolly as she gave him a good sniffing; we chatted awhile before moving on. Tramps live in many larger towns; on the whole, most are harmless lost souls who ask for little. They have given me quite a scare on occasions, like the time when I was fishing at the end of Cambridge Road. I had been fishing in the dark for about two hours with one of my younger brothers when from below me on the beach, a tramp stood up, 'Got a light mate?' He asked holding up the crunched remains of a cigarette. He had been lying beneath the wooden platform that I was fishing on without me realising; talk about giving you a heart attack. He just wandered off into the night, a plastic bag on his back carrying all the possessions he owned in the entire world.

They can be a bit profound as well. When I was a child of about ten, I was walking through the town centre and turned into part of Junction Road (long since gone to make way for our shopping centre). I came face-to-face with a drunken tramp on the pavement. He was on his knees holding on to the metal railing outside a house. He stared straight at me with his faded blue eyes; I was transfixed, like a petrified fox caught in a car's headlights. He handed me a rose, 'Give that to your mother', he said, 'As she is a beautiful woman'. Strange I thought, Mumsie's standards must have dropped a bit; I grabbed the rose and ran like the wind.

Due to these encounters in the past, I was not so surprised as I turned to continue on with my weekly walk, when the tramp shouted out to me a most profound and deep statement.
'Remember, my boy, even monkeys sometimes fall out of trees'. I still think about that, a weird but a true and deep statement. I knew all too well how quick you can go from the top to the bottom, and how when you are at the top there is only one way to go.

I walked with the warm sun on my back and the cool air filling my lungs; the smell of the wallflowers growing in the carpet gardens was mixing with the salty sea air, making an intoxicating aroma. What a joy it was to walk this promenade as people from peasants to royalty have done since Victorian times. The west part of the promenade is split into three tiers. People have told me that long ago the upper class walked the top promenade, the middle prom was for the middle class and the lower prom was for the working class. As usual the upper class got it all wrong because the lowest prom by the sea was by far the best place to walk. They must have looked down with envy at the working class, paddling in the sea and playing in the sand as they paraded in their Sunday best, parasols twirling above their lace bonnets.

My wife's grandfather Cyril, and his older brother and their father before them were responsible for the upkeep of the pretty Carpet Gardens since late Victorian times. They had kept the gardens in prize-winning condition for over 70 years. After Cyril retired he would always note that the gardens were never up to his standard when we past. Mind you, I love them. The continuous work that the council puts into them all year round really stands out in the summer. It all pays off as Eastbourne has won countless awards for their efforts.

I walked past the Bandstand, which looks like a huge meringue covered in turquoise tiles. Over the years it has seen superb open-air concerts, more often than not by military bands. There is a plaque on the wall commemorating the local musician, who played on board, The Titanic as it sank. A flock of seagulls passed me with their effortless wing flaps and their laconic cries, sounding like the end of someone laughing at an old joke, they were off to their nesting sites on the cliff faces of Beachy Head after a night's fishing in the English Channel.

On the lower promenade, just opposite the most splendid Cavendish Hotel, there is a row of iron rings set into the brickwork, by the old disconnected water fountain, where I would queue for a drink as a child. These rings are a reminder of our Victorian past. The rings were used to help pull the bathing machines in and out of the water so that the ladies could exit the bathing huts straight into the sea without being improper or un-lady like, hobbling down the stony beach. Once they had a little dip, or 'take the water' as they would say, they would climb back into the bathing hut and be pulled back up the beach with ropes through the rings, get changed and appear from the bathing hut perfectly dressed for a stroll on the prom.

Eastbourne has a special colour for all their ironwork, lamposts and railings, it is a rich blue, much like a Royal blue, but unique to our town. We, (the mutt and me) walked along, past the lifeguard Station and Life Boat Museum and the rows of tiny bathing huts that line the beach. The lamp-posts and garlands of bulbs that light the length of the prom at night were having the faulty bulbs replaced by noisy council workers that were shouting to each other from ladders leaning against the lamposts. The builders had just arrived. They were demolishing an old hotel on the corner. I remembered how once as a kid I had ran through the foyer of that hotel in a blaze of excitement. I was with my elder brother who was clutching a live 10lb cod to his chest. We had just caught it off the beach opposite and took it to show the chef, a friend of ours who never believed we caught anything. At last we had the proof, much to the astonishment of the hotel guests.

The railings as you round the corner of the Wish Tower Café; stretch the entire length of the promenade and trail off into the distance like a blue fence on a sheep farm. The Wish Tower Café is a great place to sit on a rough windy day and stare out to a wild sea, when heavy grey clouds bear down upon a furious rumbling sea, which spits back in fury at her tormentor above.

Today was the exact opposite of those stormy winters days. Out at sea I could hear the low rumble of fishing boats' diesel engines; they were out of sight, lost in the soft mist that was taking all the sharp edges off the morning and making all the sounds of the new day hush into a peaceful murmur. This time of year the boats will be after fresh crab, lobster and whelks. The spring run of bass will be in any day now once the water reaches the magical 10 centigrade mark. Bass will be after the soft back and peeler crabs that use the rocks around the coastline as their breeding grounds. The female crabs can only mate when they have a soft shell, so she seeks out the protection of the weed-covered rocks to shed her shell. The males are attracted by her scent as she sheds, but so are the hunting bass, so she has to be cunning to survive.

The hills in the distance that lead to Beachy Head and then further on to the famous Seven Sisters, were also in a hazy mist and almost lost to the eye. It would not be long before the hot sun would burn off the moisture in the mist and reveal the Downs in all their splendour. High above the outline of the cliffs, slowly slipping out of sight in the brightening day, hung a half moon in a light blue heaven.

Rolly was chasing another early morning runner, a habit she picked up, which I have not managed to break her of. It would not be so bad but, it is always the female joggers that she goes after, I promise I have not trained her to do that. This time of the morning it is nearly always the women that are out running. On my walk, eleven runners passed me, of which only one was a man. I called Rolly back and stopped to talk to a man who had just been picking winkles from the lagoon, which was slowly appearing as the tide receded. He had a small bag of winkles, just enough for a meal and was sitting on the wooden steps that lead to the beach.

'Still a bit cold for prawning' I said as I neared him.

'Yep, might be alright next week if the wind keeps off', he replied turning to talk to me and stroke Rolly. Rolly did not like the smell of the man's cigarette, which was a home-made roll up, so she ran off down the beach chasing seagulls. I stopped and chatted for a few minutes as the sun started to dry the salty wet pebbles on the beach.

I came to the end of the promenade at Holywell, some people say this place is called Holywell because the water ran clear and sweet from the hills and was used for centuries by local people who considered it a holy place. Others say  it came from the name for hole, as there was a large hole or chalk pit there, which is now pretty gardens, with a tea chalet at the bottom. I prefer the first explanation, Holywell does feel special, it always has. At the end of the promenade the beach continues along the base of the chalk cliffs where seagulls nest and chunks of flora and fauna grip the cliff face with a precarious hold. The famous red and white Beachy Head lighthouse lies just around the first turn of the cliffs. It is another hour's walk to the lighthouse over the rough beach with fresh chalk rock falls to climb over. It is a fantastic walk if you want to make a day of it, but I had work to do and had to start the journey back to my car. Rolly stood looking longingly on towards the cliffs knowing that sometimes I take her on that walk. She reluctantly turned and followed me as I made my way back towards the car.

It was around these weed beds that as children we would cover ourselves in the thick abundant seaweed, then sink down like alligators with our noses just above the water line. We would wait for an unsuspecting tourist to walk past; then, with childish glee, we would rear up, wailing like sea monsters, needless to say we did not shock too many of them.

I made my way up the steep path past the tea chalet and onward to my old school, perched on the corner of the South Downs. An impressive Victorian building that has had many a famous pupil pass through her halls. During

The Second World War although details are still shrouded in secrecy, St Bedes was reputedly one of the Naval intelligence recruiting and training bases for Britain's best kept secret of the 20th century; the Bletchley Park code breaking centre, known as Station X. Station X in Buckinghamshire, in its prime, during the last few years of the Second World War had over 10,000 people working there, it was really a hidden city of secrets. Some say the brightest young minds in the country were taken to Station X. People like Alan Turin and Tommy Flowers were considered the young Einstein's of their day, they were responsible for the World's first computers, like the huge electro mechanical machine called The Bomb, used to break the famous German- Enigma Code, and the amazing Colossus and Lorenz machines, capable of reading a German code quicker than the Germans could read it themselves. These machines were the first real computers of the modern age.

The code breakers lived secret lives in their secret city; working tirelessly to translate all the messages that the Germans and Italians were sending over the airwaves. The results were staggering. The Germans thought the codes, especially their Fish Code, were unbreakable; this was to cost them dear. Winston Churchill after the war admitted that the code breakers had shortened the war by more than two years and saved countless lives. For example, secrets from Station X, passed to British and American intelligence in North Africa were vital; Montgomery was informed of Rommel's position and his low rations, because of this, Monty (later to become Viscount Montgomery of El Alamein) pushed with all his forces and the famous battle of El Alamein was a British victory, allowing Monty to crush Rommel-the Desert Rat, forcing the remains of his shattered forces to flee. During the all-important D-Day landings, in June of 1944, Bletchley Park correctly predicted 98% of all German positions.

After the war, Bletchley Park was dismantled and destroyed, even the amazing computer machines that would have lead the world, were smashed to pieces and the plans to make them, burnt. Saving these would have meant Britain leading the way in the computer industry that was to follow decades later, but it was not to be. Station X was no more; it disappeared into a silent history, the brave men and women went back to their daily jobs at post offices, bakers, at sweet shops and grocers all over the country. They never talked about there incredible efforts in a secret city, to help bring the war to a close. The computer age was left for the Americans to nurture and develop, some say, with the technology learnt from the German code machines, the very machines that Station X was set up for in the first place.

All along the seafront there are literally hundreds of seats placed by loving relatives as a reminder of their departed ones. Most of the inscriptions are similar; for example, in fondest memory of Lilly Smith 1907-1985. However there are a few funny ones as one of the last benches on the prom announces: ' For the Barnes family, who never had time to sit down'.

This part of Eastbourne is called Meads and the very first local settlement was supposed to be around this area. Eastbourne was once no more than a small fishing community where people made their home at the foot of the hills. They had everything they could ever want here; protection from the strong winds provided by the mighty South Downs, easy access to the beach, fresh, clean water pouring from the hillside and a view made in paradise; yes, it is easy to see why Eastbourne started at this point. There is still evidence of their passing. In the lagoon where the second reef runs like a bridge across the bay, there are several channels through the rocks which the locals cut for their boats to come in and out. You can only see them at half or low tide, but they are there, testament to our old Eastbourne fishermen from a long time ago.

I walked past The Grand Hotel, Eastbourne's only five star hotel, the Union Jack was fluttering proudly above it in the gentle breeze. The building is brilliant white, reminiscent of the chalk faced cliffs, with a statue of the 7th Duke of Devonshire standing in front of the green watching all the visitors come and go. I passed the Martello Tower, built to keep that mischievous French boy, Napoleon, out of England. Now, far from the guns on its turrets, it is a puppet museum; how times have changed. Countries that once faced each other in war now swap cheeses and wines.

As I reached the top of Western Lawns the first swallows of the year came out of the mist over the sea, like tiny guided missiles. They shot past me chattering in excitement for they had made another successful journey from their winter feeding grounds in Africa. They were off to their summer nesting sites in the eves of little country cottages and church lofts all over England. Unnoticed, they flew over the tourists who by now were starting to fill the endless rows of benches. Some of the holidaymakers were having their daily struggle with the folding deckchairs that can drive an unsuspecting tourist into a right frenzy; they just cannot figure out how to unfold them. It is always a good laugh watching someone's mind at work trying to figure out something that must be simple but just won't work.

Many of the deckchairs, which are normally blue and white-striped nylon, have been replaced with lovely new deckchairs advertising Nestle Ice Cream. It will keep Ben at the Council Works, in Wartling Road busy, as the new chairs are just heavy cotton drill. This will rot very quickly with the harsh weather and sun bleaching they have to tolerate. He uses a huge Singer 32K treadle machine that is almost 100 years old but will sew anything. It is surprising how many shops, councils and hotels have machines. I visit most of them on my calls. It does not matter if it is the linen room at The Grand or the Eastbourne Bus Depot, they need sewing machines for repairs whether it is for a linen sheet or a ripped seat and thankfully they all pay for my services.

Some of the holidaymakers were reading newspapers spread across their laps, just lazing around as tourists do. 'The lucky buggers, no rush for them today', I thought as I unlocked the Land Rover and Rolly jumped in. Now off to Lincoln's for some of their hot jam doughnuts, they always have them ready for me. Then home to wash them down with a cup of fresh hot coffee, now that's what I call a good breakfast (as long as you ignore the calories). As I drove away, I was still licking my lips as the smell of frying bacon that had enticed me earlier was still lingering around the hotel entrances.

On special days like these, my work becomes second place. I have to be in the mood, until of course, I open the post and find one of those awful bills that need paying, that will inevitably get me motivated. Still, there is always next Saturday to look forward to and, come rain or shine another stroll along the prom.

*Our Grand Hotel with the Duke standing proudly in front.*
*The Grand is the only 5 star hotel in Eastbourne*

*Eastbourne Bandstand where bands still play all through the summer. John Wesley Woodward, the*
*band member who went down with the Titanic regularly played here.*

*This plaque on the Bandstand wall commemorates John Woodward who went down with the White Star Liner, Titanic on the 15th April 1912.*

*Two of the three tiers of the promenade the upper tier is just out of view. It is low tide and the rocky weed beds are exposed, the start of the South Down's is behind that leads 100 miles westward towards Winchester*

*My old school, a typical victorian boarding school. The top middle window was my dormitory. At one point there was nearly as many private schools in Eastbourne as days of the year. Some were very small, no more than a dozen pupils, some took hundreds.*

# THE LONGEST DAY

Midsummer was here; the longest day of the year had started early. The birds outside woke me with their noisy dawn chorus; it was around 3.30 in the morning. By 4.30 I was leaning out of the window watching the sun come to relieve the moon from her night-time watch. It never ceases to amaze me the magical start to a new day, witnessed by every living soul who has walked our planet, from Caesar to Napoleon, to you and me. A huge red sun was slowly lifting above the watery horizon off the coast. It was starting another of its daily travels over my tiny corner of the World, since before man, before the dinosaurs, before the very first bird lifted its head and threw music to the wind; that huge red fiery globe had been busy, never missing a day. I went back to bed and drifted in and out of sleep until the six o'clock alarm announced the start of my daily work.

An enjoyable trip through the countryside up towards Newick found me arriving at Honey Bee Cottage. I was there to fix a troublesome Bernina Sport. There was no answer from the front of the old wooden door so I walked around to the rear garden to find the family eating breakfast on the patio.

'Good morning' I perked up cheerfully at the Charles family.

Mrs Charles called me over. 'Alex, you are early as usual, would you like to join us for a bite to eat'?

The smell of fresh coffee was too much to resist, even though I had eaten my breakfast barely an hour before. 'Yes I would love to' I said as she pulled out one of the patio seats for me. Before long I was enjoying idle chat about bees and chewing on some marmalade toast. It was a superb June morning and the honeybees were busy collecting nectar for their hives on the neighbouring farm.

After a pleasant half-an-hour I started to get down to work repairing her Bernina; all went well until I came to test the machine. 'Have you got the foot control Mrs Charles', I shouted to her in the kitchen.

'Is it not with the machine'?

'The lead is, but not the foot, it must be around here somewhere'.

Well, that is what we thought; we searched high and low, even phoned the cleaner and asked her if she had moved it. Between the five of us we almost stripped the house down from top to bottom. 'Hang on' I said, 'There must be a simple answer to this dilemma, when was the last time anyone was in this room'?

'Well, on Sunday, the grandchildren were playing in here, but they would not have taken it', said Mrs Charles perplexed.

'Do they have a toy box'? I asked with a sudden rush of blood to the little grey cells.

'Yes I will fetch it'. Sure enough in the bottom of the box underneath a pile of Lego and Thunderbirds toys was the foot control. The whole family gave a sigh of relief and went back to a more relaxed manner as I finished off the Bernina.

On my way to my next customer I passed the Piltdown Man Pub. Piltdown Man was supposedly the missing link that was found near this spot. In 1912 it was a discovery, which shook the world. It was the final proof to Darwin's Theory of Evolution; the head had a jaw of an ape but the skull of a man. Charles Dawson an amateur palaeontologist (yes, I did have to look up how to spell that) discovered the million year old head in a gravel pit and before long he was giving a lecture to a packed audience at the Geographical Society in London. At last there was proof to back up Darwin's unbelievable idea of the time that we evolved from animals and not Adam and Eve. In fact, it was the cranium of a human and the jaw of an orang-utan from Borneo. However, this was not found out until 1953, so for decades the Piltdown Man was the oldest evidence of our ape ancestry, even though it was a fake. Who put the fake there is still open to discussion. There were many people who could have done it and none more famous than Sir Arthur Conan Doyle of Sherlock Holmes fame. He lived just up the road in Crowborough and penned several books that touched on the evolution of man. Sir Arthur had a keen interest in palaeontology as well as the after life and even fairies at the bottom of the garden.

As I passed through the town centre of Crowborough, Sir Arthur was standing on the corner by the traffic lights. Some local revellers the night before had put a plastic traffic cone on his bronze head and some red and white tape around his neck like a scarf. He had a Tesco's shopping bag on one arm and looked as if he had just been for a morning stroll.

'Morning Mrs Goldsmith, lovely day again', I said as I walked in, dodging the mess of toys all over the floor and a plastic car in her hallway. 'Where is the little monster then', I said looking around apprehensively.

'She is trying to see how much toast the video recorder holds in the living room, don't worry it has not worked since she poured juice over it last month', replied Mrs Goldsmith, with a past caring tone in her voice. I found Emma sitting in her nappy, munching on Marmite soldiers looking with great concentration into the mouth of the video recorder. I knelt down beside her and prised a piece of toast out of the machine and handed it to her. She beamed back as she snatched it and pushed half of it into her mouth and the other half into her cheek. Her face was a mess of Marmite and butter with crumbs stuck everywhere, she looked like the inside of a dustbin liner, while her two huge front teeth were making short work of her soggy toast.

'You won't remember me young lady as you were not even born last time I called here, but your mum and I remember it as if it was yesterday'.

I could hardly forget Emma; she had given me the fright of my life when her mum had gone into premature labour as I was fixing her machine.

'I still come out in cold sweats, you know', I said to Mrs Goldsmith as I started to work on her machine.

'Yes, looking back on it, she did give us both quite a scare, still it all worked out well in the end and guess what, I am expecting another baby in five months'.

'Wow, whatever you do, don't call me the week before the baby's due', I said with a smile. 'If you do I will turn up with towels and a mobile phone'

I waved goodbye to Emma who was at the front door being held by her mum, she almost waved back but lost interest in trying to co-ordinate her hand into a wave. I always think that babies must be the prettiest things in the world, otherwise we would never put up with all the trouble they give us. A baby can scream all day and throw up its food, fill their nappies with the most disgusting smells possible, make you walk around like a zombie for months if not years; basically turn your life upside down, but you forgive them completely and turn to mush when they smile.

I went off to visit a new customer, a very sprightly, 87 year old called Mrs Wiss. She was a skilled seamstress from the old school. She was very small, and frail, slightly bent over from arthritic joints, with large dark eyes and a long straight nose on which perched a pair of spectacles; all in all she looked rather like a field mouse. She had been taught her trade in Brighton by a French tailoress called Madame Florette. Madame Florette was an eccentric woman who had a monkey as a pet; which she took for walks along the promenade on sunny afternoons, before taking tea at The Grand. For a whole year Mrs Wiss was not allowed near a sewing machine, she had to do the ironing and folding and delivering of garments that had been made at Madame Florette's. After a year of basic learning she was finally allowed to sew herself. Madame Florette had sewn for so long that she had grooves in her teeth from holding the pins when marking out and pinning her dresses. Her dentist used to grind her teeth level when she had her check up. The monkey, which used to have the run of the house, once bit Mrs Wiss and she was petrified of the animal. Can you imagine having to keep an eye out for a monkey while you are sewing, that has got to be a first.

After fixing Mrs Wiss's Spanish Alfa machine that had simply ground to a halt from over use, she wrote me out a cheque. Her hand was shaking with age and she took ages. As she got near the end she made a mistake and ripped the cheque up. She started again and got half way through and made another mistake.
'Let me write the cheque out for you', I said hoping to get things moving. I wrote the cheque out perfectly, 'Sussex Sewing Machines', the amount, then I signed it. Damn!!!
'I don't think you wanted to do that young man', Mrs Wiss laughed. By now we had gone through three cheques and spent ten minutes doing nothing. Finally I wrote the cheque, she signed it and I hit the road to my next call.

I pulled into Willingford Lane in Burwash Weald, a lane that was made in paradise and possibly one of the finest parts of Sussex, if not the world. The lane is little more than a dirt track in places and leads from Burwash Weald down past some of Jack Cade's follies, like the Brightling Needle, before joining the road to Bodle Street Green.
'What have you done here then?' I enquired as I suspiciously turned the taped up electrical lead in my fingers.
'The kind man next door soldered the wires together for me,' she replied as if I had nothing to worry about. From the look of the bodged up wiring this was going to be a grand firework show.
'Have you tried the machine since he rewired the plug for you?'

'I was waiting for you to try it,' she replied as if thinking I was paid to take the risk. I took the bull by the horns, held my breath and plugged it in. Sure as eggs are eggs the fuses for the entire house shorted. 'What a surprise,' I said in my usual sarcastic tone as smoke came away from the side of the machine. She just looked bemused. Once again I had only come to service the machine and found someone trying to kill me. I applied a bit of logic to the problem and soon had the machine rewired correctly and running nicely. In the lounge of the cottage was a beautiful painting of an idyllic thatched cottage with numbers along the bottom edge of the painting. 'What is that all about I asked as we passed to the door, pointing to the painting?'

'That is my lottery cottage. I painted it last year and when my numbers, the ones below come up, I am going to find the closest cottage to my dream one here and live there, with my two cats and a dozen chickens'.

'Well good luck, stranger things have happened'.

I waved and as I drove off down the lane the Land Rover rolled over some fresh horse manure with a horrible squishing sound. I looked out at the side of the car and saw the muck had sprayed up along the doors; it was just the perfect consistency and unfortunately stuck to my car. 'That's a trip to the car wash or maybe I could try and bribe the kids again', I thought as I rolled down Willingford Lane towards The Swan Public House at Woods Corner.

As I drove along the bumpy road, birdsong filled my ears mixed with the distant rumble of tractors working the land. The road dropped and rose like a gentle roller coaster through the East Sussex countryside; down through woods where baby squirrels were playing in the dappled light, then back up into the bright sunlight and open farmland with majestic views beneath a cloudless sky. The ferns on the roadside were just unravelling like a green fist unclenching for the summer. Blackberry blossom was emerging from in-between the beech hedgerows with their soft tender tips of brambles pushing through the foliage, each stem held the promise of delicious fruits later in the year. A pleasant smell of wild garlic filled the air mixed with sweet chestnut and wild dog rose. What a beautiful ride, made in heaven. Perhaps when you die you are taken along such a path to paradise, for surely there is no closer match to heaven than this tranquil countryside in early summer.

I stopped for a short break to lap up this perfect day. Crows were playing high above the woods and the first Cuckoo of summer made her distinctive call. There is an old proverb that says; if you shake your loose change when you hear a Cuckoo you will never run out of money. It works for me! In the woods near where I parked, I knew the local equivalent of Bambi would be watching my every move, for this is deer country. I could not see them, but they had left fresh tracks in the soft earth where they had skipped over the fence earlier in the morning. Before long I was on the move again, down past The White Horse pub at Bodle Street Green. On the post by the village hall was a poster announcing the Summer Fete to be held on June 30th, past St John the Evangelist's church and on to Herstmonceux upon a slight rise in the distance.

I dropped down Joe's Lane and pulled up at the junction almost opposite the Tudor looking Horseshoe Inn with its superb woodwork; the entrance is a large horseshoe carved out of curving oak beams. Past Windmill Hill with the stark old mill looking very neglected on the ridge. Corrugated steel sheets cover her old wood planks and she looks like a giant tethered to the spot. As I mentioned earlier she is the last of a kind, the only windmill left that was built around a huge central spindle, so that the whole mill could turn into the wind and the sails could spin all day. She must have been an impressive sight in her heyday. On the outskirts of Herstmonceux, Reg, the old trug-maker was busy stripping lengths of chestnut down for his trugs. Sussex trugs are a kind of open shallow garden basket, which are famous throughout the country and not cheap. They will last a lifetime if you keep the woodworm away from them. The word trug comes from an old Sussex word meaning boat shaped. Reg has sat out the front of the trug shop since before I can remember. His skin is the colour of polished dark oak with a face as wrinkled as any face could be that has spent a lifetime under the Sussex sun. He has the eyes of an eagle and always gives you a friendly wave as you pass; he is a part of the character of old Herstmonceux.

There is a tale about the original inventor of The Sussex Trug, Thomas Smith. They say that Thomas won several medals for his trugs at the Great Exhibition of 1851, at Crystal Palace. Queen Victoria and her husband,

Prince Albert were most taken with some of Thomas's fancy trugs, they placed an order for him to make one for each of their children. Thomas was so proud of his order that once he had finished the trugs he placed them all in his wheelbarrow and walked the 59 miles from Herstmonceux to The Palace in London, and delivered them personally to the Queen.

My next call, to a complete stranger, started off badly. As I rang the doorbell, I felt something wet hit the side of my head. I looked across my shoulder to see dollops of bird droppings like a row of bombs, splattered over my shirt. Above the doorway nesting in the eves were some house martins. They began chattering away, probably having a good laugh at what they had done. A nice old dear opened the door; she started to laugh as she saw what had happened.

'Come in and I will wipe you off' she said turning and walking in. I followed her into the kitchen where most of the offending article was removed.

'That's nothing, you should see the side of my car, it is plastered with enough manure to plant roses,' I told her.

'We have to put up with life's little trials don't we' she said as she put the kettle on, 'Anyway it is good luck to have a bird poop on you, perhaps you will have a windfall from somewhere'.

'I don't know about windfall, I should be the luckiest man around with the amount of times that has happened to me'.

The old girl had two budgies that were flying free. They could have gone straight out of the back door which was wide open but just sat on the corner cupboard looking at me. 'Don't you worry they will disappear?' I asked enquiringly.

'Oh no, they never have; they fly around the garden but always come back. When I first got them I showed them this'. She took me into another room where, in a glass domed jar was a stuffed Spanish woodpecker. 'I told them if they flew away this is how they would end up and they have never left home'.

'Well that's a first' I said, 'Talk about shock tactics'.

I started to work on her Italian Necchi Supernova, one of the finest machines ever made, a cup of tea by my side. We chatted about her machine and all the things that she had made on it since her husband bought it for their first wedding anniversary in 1960. 'Everything from the curtains in our villa in Spain to my daughter's bridesmaids dresses have been stitched on that machine; never missed a beat in 40 years of service, I would not expect you to hear that from these new plastic machines nowadays?'

'I am afraid you are right. Very few machines made today will be around in 40 years time, they all seem to be disposable now'.

'Yes that's the problem, we are living in a throw away society and nothing is cherished anymore,' she said letting out a big sigh. The Necchi had a damaged hook that soon was straightened and smoothed down enough to produce a good stitch.

'That's strange my eye is starting to water,' she said wiping a tear away with a paper tissue.

'Don't worry that's because you have to pay me now' I said laughing as I finished writing her receipt.

'Very funny, it is that cold wind through the window, anyway I think you are worth every penny. If you had not fixed the machine I would have to buy a new one and I am very attached to my little friend'.

As I opened the front door to leave, I peeked up at the nest in the cottage eves. There were three little house martin heads peering down at me. They were still chattering away nineteen to the dozen; I am sure the little darlings were laughing at me. If I had got my hands on them, it would have been a different story, I would have one stuffed, to make a lovely accompaniment to the woman's 'stiff' Spanish woodpecker, as there was plenty of room in the glass domed jar.

Heading towards home, I was stuck in an endless queue of traffic; it was Tennis Week in Eastbourne. The town was humming with smart linen clad ladies with large hats and sunshades making their way to the tennis tournament at Devonshire Park. Tennis week is great for the town. The hotels were usually heaving and the BBC cameras were busy filming the ladies Wimbledon warm-up event.

By the time I arrived home, I was weary from a long morning of grafting. I slumped lazily into my armchair for a rest before continuing the days work. My son was banging out a tune on his guitar upstairs, so my daughter had turned up her CD player to drown out the noise. It was like coming home to an indoor concert. After a few well chosen words, the house calmed to a more suitable noise level. I watched the news on the television with interest as the Druids performed their mystical rights at Stonehenge on this, the longest day of the year. The summer solstice is their most special time and if you visit Stonehenge you will see why. In reality it is no great work of art or impressive monument like the Pyramids at Giza, or the Senate at Rome, but there is a strange magic about the place that words could never describe, a feeling or connection with a race of people that was in tune with the earth and nature. People from long ago who worshipped the seasons and the soil and lived in perfect harmony with their surroundings.

The hot summer afternoon drifted into evening and before long the sun was starting its final voyage of the day. We decided to take Rolly for a last run before bedtime up along the ridge known locally as The Saddle, which is at the top of Butts Lane. Butts Lane leads up onto the South Downs and beyond. My street was the ancient path from the Downs straight to Pevensey Castle; used by man for two millennia and the deep ruts in the flinty-chalk soil upon the hills, bear testament to the thousands of travellers that have passed before us. Now the paths are more for tourists and dog walkers than trade. The routes travelled weekly by farming folk to market have long since been forgotten. Someone once told me that the distance apart on the rails of a modern railway track are based on the cart tracks, which in turn were based on the chariot tracks used by the Romans. Proof of this is the Apian Way leading into Rome, where the grooves in the roads are exactly the same as the tracks on any modern railway; the rails simply evolved. The Apian Way is a cobbled causeway built around two thousand years ago. In the centre are chips of polished marble that catch the moonlight and shine. This in turn helps the travellers keep their carts and chariots on the road at night; here we are thinking we are so advanced; when they had it all sorted years ago.

Rolly ran in front of us as we walked along the ridge that drops down to Wish Hill and Chalk Farm below. A rooster was doing his duty crowing his heart out, letting the village know that night would soon be upon us. Rolly was busy sniffing the earth for the scent of a rabbit. The sun started dipping behind Mount Caburn on the far horizon, finishing its longest day and conceding her watch of the planet, once more to the moon. Mount

Caburn is just above Lewes, about 15 miles distant. The ridge of Downland drops suddenly to the fertile flat Sussex farmland with small patches of woods before rising sharply up to Mount Caburn. It was the site of an Iron Age Fort. Today it is just a grass mound on the top a hill.

It is not hard to imagine the guards that walked the battlements on chilly nights wondering about their loved ones warm in bed. The fort was apparently over run by the Romans, conquerors of a foreign barbaric race, who enforced their civilisation with unstoppable might and opened a new chapter in our unique history. Skylark were dropping from the sky down to their nesting sites in the lush Downland turf. They had finished composing their musical symphonies for another day. Swallows were gliding silently, cutting the cool evening air, arching in tight circles with their clothes-peg tails twitching, picking off the last remaining insects before the night stole their sight. The woodland birds were having one last singsong in the coppices that cling to the lea side of the Downs and rooks joined in 'cawing' at the sky. Below me the towns furthest away like Hastings started to fade into the night and a few lights came on around the centre of Eastbourne. We walked in silence on this the longest day of the year, capturing the splendour of the sunset that made sharp silhouettes of the trees against the skyline. A single fire from amongst the patchwork of farms in the distance lifted languidly into the sky; the whole scene viewed from so high above looked like a toy Legoland.

Dotted along the ridges around this area of the Downs are burial mounds from  distant times. They are probably Neolithic and today are no more than mounds of grass with hollows where amateur archaeologists have dug for trinkets. Around the turn of the century it became a popular pastime to walk the Downs with a picnic and have a dig for buried treasure from a long forgotten king. Luckily the sites are now protected and are left alone for us to stroll over and ponder about. There is a kind of magic about these burial sites, much like Stonehenge or the Avebury Rings; on special evenings they almost talk to you. They mark the passing of a tribal chief or an important man of the village. The huge effort required to dig into the hard soil with basic tools available to early man, like antler and pick was such an undertaking that it would only have been done for someone very special. It is the most wonderful place to have a burial site. You have majestic, timeless views that stretch out before the eye. The last mound from the car park, westward about a mile from the car, is my favourite. If I stand on it I can see the whole of my area. All the parts of East Sussex that I travel are clearly visible from here; Saltdean on the coast, right around to Uckfield, Heathfield, Crowborough on the distant skyline, sweeping across to the Coastguard Cottages on the ridge at Hastings and the tip of Dungeness Power Station just past Rye. When the sun is just right you can count all the windmills in East Sussex. I often just stand on this spot and gaze, glassy-eyed, like an old dear in a rest home, transfixed by the sheer beauty of the place.

Darkness was slowly drawing a huge quilt over the countryside and the small villages started to blend into one. They were visible only by the clumps of tiny lights in the dimness. Finally, as the sun passed below the horizon on Midsummer's Day she had one last spectacular display up her sleeve. The Western skyline lit up in brilliant reds and oranges like a great city on fire. Somewhere on the other side of the planet the first rays of light would be sneaking through the gaps in half closed curtains as their new day dawns; and so the world turns.

As we reached the fence that drops down through farmland to the excellent Eight Bells pub, darkness was with us. Before long there was little left of this Midsummer Day and the deep blue of a star-studded heaven started to become visible; a single plane headed for the continent, it streaked across the sky, leaving a white vapour trail like a comet. We made our way home; I glanced at my watch, it was 9.45pm. Turning back, we walked into the wind that had cooled from the heat of the day; it washed me with the sweet scent of wild honeysuckle that tangles the bushes in the vale like a bad hair day. The wind also held a hint of camomile and thyme that grows low to the ground amongst the vetch and buttercups. There seems to be a thousand different plants and flowers that grow profusely amongst the Downland turf, and like many that have walked before me, I have no idea of their names, but take great pleasure in them.

The trees and bushes along the ridge are swept over from the fierce south-westerly winds that race up from a huge cleft in the Downland leading to the hamlet of Birling Gap and then the English Channel beyond. On certain days when the wind is wild, if you walk to the centre of The Saddle where the wind is at it strongest, you can lean at almost 45 degrees into it. Being so high on the Downland, it is the closest feeling you will ever have of being like a bird, the wind makes your eyes water and you feel as if you have been lifted above the World, to soar like an eagle, (in my case a rather heavy eagle), it is pure pleasure.

As we got back to the car, streams of headlights from late commuter traffic were visible on the A22 heading North and home for another day. Out at sea, lights from fishing boats twinkled like fallen stars in a watery heaven. A fox was hunting, keeping close to the bushes, zigzagging in and out hoping to rustle up a rabbit for supper. They have a good life here on the Downs, it is like having an over stocked larder, some say there are as many as two million rabbits on our part of the Downland. We jumped into the Land Rover and headed down the steep track home for a well-deserved cuppa, as we hit the main road, the yellow sodium street lamps lit our way. It had been an extraordinary day; I had been up for over 18 hours and loved every second of it. Midsummer the longest day, the 21st of June 2001 in East Sussex was almost over but never, ever, forgotten.

Willingford Lane...

*Sunset over the Down's - pure magic and it happens every single day*

*Combine harvesters busy at work on the rich Sussex soil*

Many of my poems are quite dark and deep but this is a sweet little poem that I wrote around the middle of summer many years ago.

# MIDSUMMER'S NIGHT

*Star shine-moon bright,*
*In the quietest hour,*
*At the dead of night,*
*Little Poppy field mouse*
*Comes out to play.*

*Up through the cornfield,*
*Planted by farmer Brown,*
*Into the green weald*
*Of our South Down.*

*Little Poppy field mouse,*
*Is looking far and wide,*
*Over Butts Brow*
*And down the other side.*

*She is getting closer now,*
*Her heart is beating fast,*
*And there they all are,*
*She's arrived at last.*

*Round and round they dance,*
*At the bottom of the hill,*
*Under bright moonbeams,*
*It gives her such a thrill.*

*Later, homeward bound she rushes,*
*Along the Babylon Track,*
*Scampering through Cold Crouch,*
*Making her way back.*

*Back to her little home,*
*In the corner of a field,*
*To dream of midsummer's night,*
*Upon the Sussex Weald.*

*Alex I. Askaroff*

# PEACEHAVEN PANSIES - THE RETURN

High summer was here, swifts played upon cloudless thermals, skylarks sang with abandon, hovering above the parched Downland which had turned from a lush green to a dusty brown; the soil lay cracked open like dying legionnaires gasping for water in an African desert. Crickets rubbed up their busy legs and chattered away amongst the meadow thistle in the high grass. Most of June had passed without a drop of rain and July started much the same, the countryside had long forgotten the relentless deluges of winter. The mock orange had left its scent as a memory and the white cups of the bindweed littered the untrimmed roadside hedges. The last bells of foxglove hung to the tips of their long straight stems, like the final stop on an elevator and within days they to would be gone; after the first downpour they will totter at precarious angles, like gravestones in an old churchyard. The brambles had silently and persistently crept through the dense foliage, tiptoed into the light and offered up their pale fruits in worship to the sun. It would be another two months before their berries turn to a succulent black gold so dearly sought after by foraging wildlife, jam makers and the odd blackberry wine fanatic.

Beekeepers all over Sussex were busy collecting their first donations of honey. Their hives that were dotted around the countryside in hidden corners of gardens and fields were painstakingly being filled with nectar by the worker bees. Someone once told me it takes nectar from a million flowers to produce one jar of honey. It is one of those amazing facts that we take for granted.

As I walked down the path of the Peacehaven bungalow something seemed ominously familiar but I could not put my finger on it. I rang the bell and through the frosted half glass door I saw a large bulky shape move menacingly towards me; I suddenly remembered where I was, but it was too late.

'Hello my dear' came a low, husky voice, 'how nice to see you again, put a little weight on have we'?

I was confronted by a startling pink dressing gown, wrapped around a wobbly man with unshaven bristles pushing through at least five layers of make up.

'Oh no!' It had all come back in a horrifying flash of reality. I had called on

the two cross-dressing Brighton bartenders... there was no way out!!!!!
'Hi' I said trying not to let my voice go all squeaky, which it does when I become alarmed. 'Having a problem with the machine again?' I managed to stutter out.
'Her ladyship is in the parlour having one of her tantrums, he will tell you all about it, in you go now, chop, chop',
I walked along the corridor with growing apprehension, like a slave into the arena in Rome.
'Ah dear boy, I am so glad to see you. Look what has happened to my machine, without her I feel about as useless as a one legged man at an arse kicking contest'

In the parlour, as they liked to call their lounge, the Jones machine sat patiently waiting for my help. I could see the problem; a blunt needle had pushed some fine silk through the needle plate and jammed the machine. 'You must be careful with that blouse, I am wearing it to work tonight' came a voice from behind me. I swung round as I felt Rosie's breath on my neck. I managed to slither around to the side of the table and wriggle into some space; a wicked gleam was in Rosie's eye. This was as bad as the last time when I was here, that time my heart had missed a beat for a week.
'Now, now Rosie calm down, put the pot on and make us all a nice brew', said Charlie.
'I thought his name was Bert', I whispered to Charlie when we were alone.
 'Oh yes, what a good memory you have young man, his real name is Bert', said Charlie in a hushed tone, 'Rosie is his 'stage name', fits him much better don't you think'? He said, swirling around and dropping his arm in a graceful bow. 'He is only teasing you, he is quite harmless really, we have been together for over 23 years, he is like my pet dog' Charlie said flashing his over large, false eyelashes at me. 'I feed him twice a day and he is happy'. Charlie sauntered off, 'Excuse me now, my boy, while I slip into something a little cooler'. I did not like the sound of that at all. I looked up the corridor towards the front door and wondered if I should make a break for it while the coast was clear. I had not yet unpacked my tools so I could have quite easily sidled off. But I felt a pang of guilt looking at the blouse that was stuck in the machine and knowing how desperate Rosie looked at me, desperate and lustful. I just had to ignore the lustful bit and get down to work!

Rosie appeared carrying a tray with a shocking pink tea cosy covering a Portmeirion teapot, three cups and a packet of McVitie's Digestive biscuits. As she, I mean he, placed it on the pretty oval tea table, I managed to loosen the needle and undo the hook mechanism beneath the machine; with a little dexterity the blouse came away from the machine.

'Oh you clever boy', cried Rosie in an overjoyed state, She grasped the silk and held it up to the satin covered lamp in the corner. 'Hardly a mark on it, oh I could kiss you'.

'That's ok, there really is no need for that' I squeaked, my throat restricted with my voice sounding unnaturally high like a schoolboy who had been evicted from the school choir.

Suddenly, from a corner room, Charlie swanned in, he had 'slipped into' a white cotton shirt, opened to the waist and had prised his rather considerable girth into a pair of skin-tight shiny black shorts that squeaked as he walked and to finish off, a pair of fluffy pink slippers. He looked perfectly at home in their flamboyant surroundings, he laughed out loud as he saw my jaw drop. 'I wish I had that effect on all the boys', he said as he sauntered up to Rosie.

'Well how do I look darling', he said parading in front of Rosie.

'They look rather a squeeze', replied Rosie.

'Yes, you're right sweetie', said Charlie pulling on the crotch of his shorts and squinting as if he was sucking lemons. 'They are a bit tight up the Khyber Pass'.

Charlie squeaked over to examine the damaged blouse. 'Oh that will be fine, darling' he called to Rosie. 'Once you have finished the last seam you will look like an angel'.

The thought of angels looking like the 'Peacehaven Pansies', Charlie & Rosie, was not worth thinking about. A shudder ran down my spine with images of two fat blokes trying to fly with their new wings that Gabriel had just bestowed upon them. They both saw the smile on my face and looked at me with raised eyebrows.

'Well, ducky you never know, stranger things have happened', said Rosie. 'Now be a dear Alex, finish off this seam for me', he said handing me back the silk blouse.

'I may be good at fixing machines but sewing is another art altogether', I said.

'Oh, go on, you are just being modest, we will make sure you do it right'. At this point they both came over and stood next to me, Rosie showed me where the final seam was and I nervously started to sew along it. Half way along Charlie put his hand on my shoulder and the seam, which was going surprisingly well, suddenly skewed off the fabric.

'Now look what you have made him do', Rosie said, slapping Charlie's bottom with a whack that sounded like a whip cracking off rawhide.

'Bitch' Charlie screamed.

'Serves you right for wearing those tight pants', Rosie retorted, flicking his head backward with an arrogant twist.

'Now leave the poor boy alone, go and do something useful, your legs need waxing'.

Charlie crept off like a scolded animal.

'Charlie is like my pet dog you know', said Rosie.

'Well', I thought at least they both have the same idea about each other, they both think they are each other's pet dog. Yes, a couple of old dogs, that describes the pair perfectly.

'I am nearly finished, do you want me to run down this seam as well, it looks a bit loose'?

'Certainly, young man, finish it off nicely, I want to look my best for the show tonight. We are doing our 'Marlene' act at the pub and it goes down a storm with our loyal groupies'. I dreaded to think what they would look like, singing their hearts out in a smoke filled pub; two over ripe men, with voices like ashtrays, draped in silk.

I felt more comfortable with just Rosie in the room. At least I could keep an eye on him. In record speed I finished the seam and was packing all my tools away.

'You have not touched your tea', Rosie said.

'I'll have a sip now, I don't drink too much in the mornings,' I lied.

'Ooh I know, it makes me pee too', replied Rosie, puckering up his lips.

'Not as much as beer does', shouted Charlie who had been listening in the other room.

'Quiet or you will get another slap',

'Promises, promises', came the reply in a taunting voice.

I quickly took a sip and wrote out the invoice; Rosie fetched his purse and pulled out some money.

'Thank you, Rosie', I said.

'You can call me Bert, all my real friends do'.

'Well, thanks Bert'.

At this point Charlie ran into the room pushed his bum out at me and shouted, 'Don't thank me, just spank me'.

That was it, I was now in full blown panic mode and needed to get out of the place and fast. I grabbed my tools, tripping on one of the brightly coloured rugs that were scattered all over the floor. I headed for the door as fast as I could go with all my bits and pieces; I had two large boys in pursuit hard on my tail.

'Let me get that for you', Rosie said edging past me to the door.

'Now don't be a stranger, pop in any time, Charlie makes the best raspberry pavlova this side of Brighton'.

I squeezed past him and felt Charlie's hand on my bum; I leapt up the few steps and almost cleared the gate without opening it. I turned at the top and saw both the men killing themselves with laughter, they knew I was scared stiff and played me like a top. Charlie was laughing so hard that he started to cough and Rosie was slapping him on the back with vigour. 'Spit it out dear, spit it out'.

The milkman was coming up the street, fag in his mouth and a wire crate with four pints of gold top, full cream milk rattling in it.

'They been teasing you?' he asked as he saw my red face and the two at the door. 'Right pair of monkeys those two, come on now lads, behave yourselves', he said as he went down the steps to their door. 'If you don't, I will switch your gold top to semi skimmed for a week'.

'Oooh, who's a meanie then', they both said in perfect unison as Rosie pulled the milk from him with defiance.

That was the last I saw of them, as by now I had jumped into the Land Rover and was desperately trying to start the car. I kangarooed off up the road and parked around the corner, they had done it again, that was twice in two years. I made a mental note to make sure I remembered their address; because as sure as the sun comes up, I knew I would be back there again and next time I must be prepared for Rosie and Charlie, the 'Peacehaven Pansies'.

*Local wildlife, the Downland's are home to millions of rabbits, a tasty meal. Rabbits were once for the gentries table only, poaching rabbits was strictly controlled, if you were caught for poaching you could be deported to Australia*

*Pevensey Castle under attack again, these enthusiastic medieval actors love their work. We look on in amazement and wonder what goes on in their heads, it is great fun.*

# ANNIE'S STORY

Occasionally, I meet someone who tells the most wonderful tales of their early life. Annie Walker was one such person; she has sewing in her blood. Annie had married a garage mechanic, Horace Mason, in September of 1930 and he taught her how to look after her sewing machine; in fact he taught her how to take everything apart and put it back together again. He and his dad (also Horace) had the only garage south of the river in London that could service compression brakes (whatever they were). All the men in his family had been named Horace and all the women Julie. This was a time-honoured tradition that went back a thousand years or more. Because of the high mortality rate amongst families it was the only way of ensuring that the family name continued; as long as one member lived, then the name Horace or Julie lived on with them. Mind you it caused great confusion at Christmas time; 'here is a present for Horace, no, not that Horace, the other Horace'. It is why in some communities they used nicknames. So Horace in this story would have been called Horace the car, because he fixed cars, or you could have Horace the spade because he was a gardener. The one, always in trouble, was Horace the goat, no need to say any more on that subject.

It was because of Annie's handiwork that I first met her. Back in the 1980's she had taken the hook assembly out of her Singer 99k and could not get it back in again. It is a job that would make anyone squirm.

When I met Annie she was in her eighties, but it was not until a recent visit, just before her 93rd birthday that she told me about her early years as a court dressmaker. It is funny how sometimes old people sit silently for hours, then one day start to talk and out comes the most fascinating stories. Annie now lives in a small one-bedroom, warden assisted flat in Uckfield. Her belongings are all crammed into the main living room. The room is full of memorabilia from her long journey through life; things that if we saw them in a jumble sale, we would not give a second glance; like the old faded pictures of lost loved ones that sit on the television and mantelpiece. These things that mean little to us are irreplaceable to Annie, small mementoes of her life. We all have them, an object here or there that brings back a special memory, perhaps a holiday from long ago or a party with friends. Annie's flat was a compact version of her life; she had surrounded herself with everything that she really loved for her final years. This is her story.

Annie started sewing young; in fact, she was four years old when she had her first lesson. It all came about because of a German bomb. One night around the end of 1914, airships crept over London and dropped incendiary bombs over the city. One of the bombs exploded in the street next to her's. The vibration shook all the gas lamps in their street. Annie's family all rushed down to the cellar and even though Annie at the time was only four, she remembered her dad pulling on his trousers over his pyjamas and rushing out of the house. Annie ran upstairs after the bombing had finished and watched her dad with his neighbour, Bill Law, shimmying up the lamp-posts and lighting all the gas lamps so as not to cause any more explosions.

During the First World War Annie lived with her mum, who was heavily pregnant and dad. They lived in Murchison Road in Leighton, a suburb of London, right next door to the police station. After the bombing incident, which wiped out the street next to theirs, her parents thought it wise to evacuate from their London home. They went to live with her grandparents in Essex. The grandparents had a small cottage that backed onto the forest; which was part of a large estate. Granddad, who she still refers to as 'grandpa', was the estate manager. He looked after the old Lord who owned the large manor and grounds. Inside the small cottage it was a real squeeze, but before long they found a solution. In Englands Lane, there was an old lady with a large house. She allowed Annie's family to have the run of half the house. At the time Annie's mum was bedridden in the late stages of pregnancy with Annie's sister, and so could not look after her. The old lady who was a partial invalid did not know what to do with little Annie, but Annie's 'Granny' knew exactly what to do, she would teach her how to sew and continue the family tradition.

At the age of four Annie was no stranger to needlework, her mother sewed professionally, as did her aunt and her grandmother. Her grandmother and aunt were trained 'altar women'. They sewed for the church, anything from altar gowns and altar cloths, to cassocks and many other very special garments that were brought to them for repair. Garments that had been worn by priests and bishops for hundreds of years were painstakingly repaired by hand; they even used real gold thread. Because of their skill the garments came from all over the country from various churches and cathedrals. Their parents in turn had taught them in the early eighteenth century and theirs had taught them. It was an age-old skill, known only to a few, passed down from mother to daughter for centuries.

Her grandmother was teaching Annie an art that was going to stay with her for 90 years. Annie was first taught how to knit, and before long she was knitting on fine steel needles for the soldiers fighting in the war. She made bandages of white cotton, patches for their eyes and elbows. When bandages were no longer needed they turned to making new clothes for Annie's dolls. From that early age Annie had a love of needlework.

'I am going to put a few wrinkles in your bum before you leave me Annie', her grandmother used to say to her. Her way of telling her she was going to learn something new. For every new thing she taught Annie, she said Annie would get another wrinkle in her bum.

When the war came to and end, they packed up and moved back to 'the smoke'. As Annie left her grandmother for the last time, they were on the railway station platform waiting for the 'London Hourly'. She held Annie close and hugged her. Annie's head was snuggled into the fox fur coat that her grandmother always wore on special occasions. Her grandmother whispered in her ear, 'My darling, you are another stitch in life's rich tapestry, make the most of it'. Annie never saw her grandmother again but remembers that hug and those words. Sometimes as she falls asleep, she hears her grandmother speaking to her, and the clicking of her needles as she chatted away.

Annie went back to her London school and carried on where she had left off. At 14, the time came for Annie to enter the real world. 'You had to work for a living in those days' she told me. After a year working as a cashier, she decided that she would like to sew for a living; she had remembered all the old tricks her grandmother had taught her. Her mum managed to get her an apprenticeship at Lillytrades of London. They had a big department store in Grosvenor Street. Annie sailed through her interview. Mind you having a pedigree going back over centuries would impress any interviewer.

By the early 1930's Annie, now 20, was married to Horace and had progressed to one of London's premier fashion houses, Paris Trades. At Paris Trades, Annie started another six-year apprenticeship as a seamstress; it did not matter that she was already very skilled. You had to do it their way or not at all. She was learning more skills that would last her a lifetime. The store was along Barclay Street, which was lined with popular fashion stores, dress shops and tailors to the gentry. The sewing room, as in all the shops, was on the top floor. That is much the same as it is today and it keeps me fit climbing all those stairs in the various shops that I visit in my area. Across from Annie, on the other side of the street were other shops in competition. On more than one occasion when the shops were creating for a big event, they would all drape dark material over their windows so that no one could peek at what was being made and for whom. Such as the time when they made curtains for the dowager Queen's apartments, the windows were blanked off for a week. Each sewing room had a pair of powerful binoculars at the ready in case something was carelessly left out and they could get an eyeful of the competition. After work, many of the sewing girls were good friends and spent hours gossiping about whom they were making garments for and where they would be wearing them. So, as much as the shops tried to keep secrets, it was all a bit of a waste of time really. Mind you, had they been caught they would have been dismissed instantly.

In the 1930s, when Annie worked at Paris Trades, twice a year at the Palace, the King and Queen held special balls. The debutante balls were really to show off the breeding stock of wealthy England and get them to mix together. It was the night of the year when a wealthy young woman could meet a wealthy young man at the Palace under the gaze of royalty. One ball for the aristocracy and one for the new rich; the businessmen who had made a fortune and wanted to get up the social ladder, both balls were very important events as the new rich were the new blood off England and the aristocracy-the old. The run-up to these social gatherings was Paris Trades' busiest time of the year, even busier than Christmas. On the shop floor, silks and satins would be shown, books of all the latest fashions would be opened to excited women's eyes, measurements would be taken and whipped up to the sewing rooms. Curtains would be hung across the windows to hide away the secret gowns from prying eyes. On average, a ladies gown for the debutante ball at the Palace would take four fittings to get it just perfect. However, there was always the troublesome girl that would shed weight frantically for her big night and would need several more last minute fittings and alterations.

On these occasions at Buckingham Palace the air was electric. No sooner had the girls finished sewing for the day, at around six in the evening they would all meet up on the corner of Barclay Street. They would be wearing their best clothes, as this was a special night for the sewing girls, as well as the debutantes. Around twenty to thirty girls from the shop would scamper off up the Mall and head for the gates of the Palace. You have to remember they were all involved in the dresses from the first floor, to the top. At the gates to the Palace stood the guards and a long procession of grand cars. Down The Mall, Bentleys, Daimlers and Rolls Royce's would line the road, slowly trailing one by one into the Palace. All the girls, including the hundreds of girls from all the other London fashion houses would wander down The Mall. They would stare into the cars looking for the dresses they had made. This made the whole event for the girls so special, also for the girls in the cars. This was the best part of the evening, being stared at by all the passers by as you made your way into the ball. Why not stare; this was a special event on a special night and they were special people going to meet the King and Queen in their very best frocks and gowns, the men in their finest suits, all prim and proper. If one of the girls recognised her dress she would shout to all the others. 'Look mine is in car number seven, I made that one, isn't it beautiful, isn't it grand'. Of course you have to remember, the sewing girls never saw the woman who was in the shop, they would be upstairs, well away from the shop floor where the measurements were taken. Sometimes, a princess would wear the dress that a simple sewing girl had made, for sixpence a day, on the top floor of a dressmakers shop. When one of the dresses was spotted as many as a hundred girls would rush down The Mall and hustle to see into the window of the limousine. This was their first and last chance to see their handy work. Annie told me the Palace balls were the 'night of nights', the best night of the year.

Back at work the next day, they would all catch up with each other, talk about the night before and whom they had seen. You have to remember the aristocracy were much like film stars are today. They were the people who everybody talked about and what filled the daily newspapers. It would be another decade before the slow decline of the aristocracy started to be replaced by Hollywood gossip. Until that time, they ruled supreme and what they did, with whom and where, was all anyone wanted to know.

Twice a year at the Paris Trades, a Singer man would appear and service all the machines. He would always be wearing a white, half-length coat and a straw bowler hat. He would spend the day sorting and servicing the machines before disappearing for another six months. Annie remembers, that at Paris Trades, you only ever got a pay rise once a year and that was on your birthday. If you did not ask for a rise on that day, then you had to wait for another year. It was a hard day if you did not get the increase, or if they did not think you had worked well enough to deserve a rise. Many a girl's birthday ended in tears. They were not all happy memories.

By the beginning of the Second World War, Annie had left Paris Trades, had a daughter and set up her own business. Her first machine, a Singer 66K, had been bought from a Jewish owned sewing shop in the East End. Now I have heard a very similar story to Annie's one, it was in my last book, Random Threads, Patches of Heaven. I can't help wondering if Annie bought her sewing machine from the very same Singer shop.

Because of the very high prices that Singer machines were, they were often paid for on the never-never. Every week, without fail, Annie would go up to the shop and pay her 'three shillings and sixpence'. On the final day as she made her last payment the shopkeeper asked her to step into the back of the shop. He closed the door behind her and as her eyes became accustomed to the light, sitting next to an oil lamp in the shadows was the father of the shopkeeper. He was a white haired, long bearded old man in black attire complete with hat. His face was lit only on one side by the oil lamp.
'Please, take a seat Mrs Mason' (as she was now called). Annie sat down on an old squeaky chair beside a large square table with an old worn leather square insert in it. On the table, lit by the oil lamp was a large book. The book was full of entries in a row. The old man ran an inky finger down the list. 'Mrs Mason, this is a list of all the payments that you have made for your Singer over the years. Do you know that you have never missed a single payment'?

'I have tried really hard to keep everything up to date' Annie replied. The old Jewish shopkeeper pulled out his bottom drawer and lifted a bottle of port onto the table, followed by two glasses.

'I would like to have a drink with you to celebrate this final payment, if you would be so kind as to join me'?

'Certainly', Annie replied.

'As a show of appreciation, we at the firm would like you to keep your final payment', said the old shopkeeper. He held up his drink in salute to Annie and her regular payments. They sat together for a few minutes in idle chat before the old gentleman rose and held the door open for her. She left the shop with a large grin on her face and slightly 'tipsy'. Later, with her saving, she treated the family to lovely fish'n'chips for supper.

As time went by, Annie started passing down the secrets of her trade to her daughter, another generation, slowly and surely was learning her timeless art. Annie had started a little shop in Hampstead. Horace had unfortunately passed away from TB after being called out one winter to fix a broken down car. Annie kept the family going on her own and money coming in.

Her reputation was well known and in 1952 she was asked to make a Coronation gown for a courtier to wear at Queen Elizabeth's Coronation. The gown was for the Marchioness of Aylesbury. When the gown was finished the old Marquis was so pleased with it that he invited Annie and her daughter to the House of Lords for afternoon tea. Annie had no idea how to get into the House of Lords, as it was not the sort of place you just popped in for tea everyday really. She had the idea of treating themselves to a taxi. Once at the 'House', the Marquis was summoned and he toddled out to meet them.

'A dear old chap', Annie described him as, 'He was from the Old World, a Victorian World'. He took them into the tearoom at the House of Lords. Sitting next to them having tea was Lord Montgomery. Lord Montgomery was a war hero and in his prime. He sat looking splendid and majestic, sipping tea with the other Lords in the house. Annie's daughter was a great fan of Monty's and was all-of-a-quiver with excitement. She whispered to the old Marquis 'Isn't that Lord Montgomery sitting over there'.

'Oh yes it is my dear, but unfortunately I don't know any of these young blades today'. They all had a giggle and carried on with afternoon tea.

Knowing the old Marquis, he gave Annie an introduction to his family and when the Marchioness was in London, they would meet up at the Grosvenor Hotel. Annie would have tea, then take measurements for her new clothes. Back at her workshop she would make all the new items; once finished they would be posted off to the family in Wellingborough.

One day Annie decided enough was enough; sewing was becoming hard work for little reward. The flamboyant 1930's had slid downward to the war in the 1940's and then the austere 1950's; all the balls had stopped, as it seemed inappropriate when times were so hard. Annie had sewn for a living for decades and decided to pack it all in, never to sew commercially again; although she would make many more dresses and garments, they were only made for pleasure.

Annie was full of the memories of old London, times that we see captured on film and in pictures were times that she had lived through. There were good times and bad. She remembers vividly all three queens attending the Kings funeral, mother, wife and daughter, our Queen Elizabeth. They were all dressed in black in the now famous Widows Weeds, immortalised in film. Annie was there following the procession. She heard the wheels roll over the cobbles and the horses tread upon the stone, she knew the women who had made the dresses for this solemn occasion.

When Annie retired, she went out with a bang. Her final dress was for a very special occasion indeed, her daughter's wedding and so she finished her career in the sewing trade on a high point.

I loved hearing Annie tell me of her life, happy days and sad, happy memories and bad, they all go into making a person. We are all really just our memories; I am so glad that she shared hers with me.
'Well now,' she said as she finished her little tale, 'I think I have gone and put a wrinkle or two in your bum'.
'If you have Annie', I replied, 'It was well, well worth it'.

*My old school friend, Nelson and my son, Tom, watching the shoals of mackerel at Langney Point.*
*Yana and I caught enough for supper. There are times when you just need to get away from work*
*and fishing off the Eastbourne beaches is always relaxing.*

*Mackerel are one of the tastiest fish, but must be eaten fresh.*
*We went home and all tucked in to a fish supper that evening.*

# DIFFERENT DAYS

The people I meet constantly amaze me; some are good, some bad, and some indifferent. There are days, even weeks that go by in the same humdrum fashion when out of the blue you meet someone who tells you a story that whisks you away to another time and place. Sam Royal was one of those people.

I had come from the most hideous smelling bungalow that had been made into what can only be described as a sort of cats home. The smell was so bad I could hardly breathe and had to take short breaths. I kept going out to the car, making excuses to get things, just so I could take in fresh air. Now that may sound like an exaggeration but it was true, the smell of dozens of cats that had peed, sprayed and dumped everywhere, was something better forgotten. As I moved on to my next call I had all the windows in the Land Rover open as the smell was clinging to my clothes.

When I arrived at Sam's house, his wife had gone shopping and left him with instructions; I was to repair and service the machine and he was to make sure that it sewed before paying me. It is often the case with a new customer that they are quite distrusting. Well, I set to work and Sam put the kettle on; he was getting on in years but was still quite a fit small man, bald, with hearing aids propping up both ears. As he sat down to drink his coffee we started chatting, putting the world to right, the conversation drifted onto Norway. I had been to Norway and travelled down from Trondheim to Oslo many years ago and so was familiar with some of the areas that he had been to. Sam, it transpired, like my father, had fought with the resistance in the Second World War; while my dad was up to all sorts of tricks in Vienna, Sam was doing much the same in Norway. It had all started one day when a telegram arrived on board his ship.

Sam was working as a seaman aboard a frigate, with our Russian Allies, out at Archangel Naval Base in the North Atlantic. One day there was a message from British Intelligence for him to contact The Home Office and return immediately to London. Sam had no idea why they wanted him, but before long he was standing in a London office being briefed on his new role in the war. Sam had been picked for only one reason, his looks. He was tall, blonde and had blue eyes and looked, to all intents and purposes, like a Scandinavian. Over the next two years he was taught to speak perfect Norwegian and trained in espionage.

In early 1945 he was dropped along with a cell of six other team-mates behind enemy lines in Norway. His mission was to take out German communications, just before the allied invasion of Norway. He had specific targets that we had better not mention, but they were extremely important. After the main D-Day invasions began across Europe, Norway was next. Sam and his team had, with the help of the Resistance been hiding in the Norwegian hills waiting for their signal to act. When the time came, they carried out their mission with great success, virtually eliminating the Germans' ability to call in reinforcements; the invasion was underway and occupied Norway would soon be free again. Apparently the Germans used X-rays for their radar, unlike our system. After the main attack the scientists working on the German radar were taken to England and America to work with our scientists. Today every airport in the world is running on the systems that were developed by these liaisons.

The losses were high; Sam was the only member of his team that survived their mission. After the war, King Harald of Norway awarded Sam a medal. Many years later, Sam made a journey, more like a pilgrimage, back to Norway and handed his medal back to the Naval Institute. At the institute, while he was staring at a picture of the old King Harald, four naval officers came up to him and asked him if he remembered the old king.
'You never forget a man like that', he replied, 'We fought and died for him'.

Half a century has gone by, Sam had changed from a tall handsome blonde to a frail old man; mankind had all but forgotten about the sacrifices made by men like him. Men, because of their courage and endurance freed the World for the generations that followed.

So you see, meeting people like Sam, for me, really does make everyday different. Needless to say you can tell which I would prefer, an old war hero or a stinky cats' home.

# PILGRIMAGE

One Sunday each year, my wife Yana, and I escape for an early morning hike to one of our favourite spots in Sussex. We leave the kids snoring in bed, oblivious to the sunrise; strap the mutt into her harness (no, not Yana, the dog) and head for Mount Caburn on the outskirts of Lewes. Mount Caburn is one of the highest spots in our area and although quite a walk, is well worth it.

As we left Eastbourne towards the A27 Lewes-Brighton road, we hit traffic caused by road-works building the new bypass. Great earthmovers had converted the old chicken farm and meadow into a mush of dead earth. The place looked like the trenches from a war movie, no living thing would survive the onslaught. Soon concrete and tarmac would replace the meadow grass that used to capture the morning dew before releasing it to the sweet breeze. It is necessary, for it is progress, progressing to what we are not sure. I for one am in two minds, fed up with the traffic jams that we have suffered over recent years as Eastbourne grows, but desperately missing the old days when there was little traffic and Eastbourne was no more than a small seaside resort.

No sooner were we away from Eastbourne than we almost magically dropped back to more tranquil scenery. The Long Man at Wilmington watched from his hillside resting place as we trundled past towards Mount Caburn. We turned off the A27 through the beautiful small village of Glynde; winner of the 'best' small village or some other award like that. You can see why, it is a near perfect impression of what we would like our villages to be, quaint cottages of Sussex flint and pretty gardens. In the centre of the village, just over the small river and past the Old World railway station is the village green and cricket pitch. Sliding up the hill you pass the church and Glynde Manor, then a few farm buildings and once more you are back into the countryside.

Before long we had past a field full of Alpaca's, what they were doing around here, heaven knows, but they seemed happy enough on the Sussex turf. Then, past the world famous opera house of Glyndebourne, and onto a little cut-in at the side of the road where we parked the car. From here it was all on foot. Just as the Romans may have walked to the fort nearly two thousand years ago, so were we, mind you we did not have to walk from Italy!

We walked up a narrow flint and chalk track that wound its way upward past a small coppice that lies to the side of the hill and onwards to the high ground. Normally the coppice would have been full of birdsong but soaring in the sky was the reason all was quiet. A Golden Buzzard was making lazy wide circles in the sky above. It was making its distinctive 'peeiou' cry like a lost soul pining for love. It is one of the loneliest sounds in the World and you cannot help wondering what had made a creature make such a sad call. It was most unusual to see such a large hunting bird in our area, rising up on early thermals, quartering the fields and woodland below. They are normally more at home further down the West Country towards Dorset and Cornwall. It was probably the hot dry weather and the continuous westerly breeze that had brought the large bird so far from its usual hunting ground. No doubt when the weather and wind turns it will twist its huge wings, cry to the heavens and head for home.

The wonderful Sussex Downlands are home to some of the finest sheep in the land. The Sussex lamb is wide and plump; they are at home amongst the rich grasslands where they roam freely. Many of the local sheep are descended from original Southdown breeds, bred by farmer John Ellman in the 18th century. He became famous throughout the land for breeding high quality mutton with exceptional wool. In the churchyard at Glynde he has an impressive tomb to mark his passing. A mother sheep and two of her spring-born youngsters watched us with interest as we passed along the track; they showed no fear at our passing, just mild curiosity.

We slowly meandered along the winding track up to the high country, where the air was clear. As we reached a long ridge, huge landscapes opened up before us. You feel immortal in a place like this, gazing down on villages and farms below. The dry summer grass was noisy underfoot as we walked towards the ancient hill fort. A Chalk Hill Blue butterfly that I call Sussex Blue, danced in front of us as we walked. There was a profusion of butterflies, an entomologist's dream (OK, so that was another word I had to look up), at least thirty different kinds all busy in the early morning, collecting nectar from the vast variety of wild flowers that were silently enjoying the summer. I could just imagine a Victorian amateur butterfly collector armed with his net, leaping all over the Downland chasing these little pretty insects, only to stick a pin through them and send them to a London museum. The old name for butterfly was actually flutterby, which describes these little pretties so well. The Downlands are also home to over 150 different species of birds, so the entomologist would be trampling over the ornithologist who would be hiding in the undergrowth, twitching.

The buzzard had disappeared, lost in the distance, and the thick warm breeze once again filled with birdsong as the skylark and song thrush rose from their hiding places. The wind rustled the dry grass like a far away prairie and the hum of a thousand busy insects lifted above the ancient hillside. Thistledown tumbled over the summer flowers, teased by the gentle wind that was to guide them silently to pastures new. Large dragonflies hovered, darting this way and that sweeping up and down the path like flower fairies in a secret garden. What a day it was and what a place to be.

Before long we had made our way to the top of Mount Caburn. It sounds like a great mountain, but in reality it is no more than a gentle peak on a hill, a few hundred feet above sea level and a most perfect site for a fort. The hilltop fortress roots go way back to the Neolithic period, with some burial mounds still in evidence around the area. In the Iron Age the hilltop fortress would have sheltered the surrounding villages in times of danger. Many say that it was the site of a Roman fort for many years. You can see why, as from this point you would see over your dominions below and they in turn would look up in awe at your might; a constant warning that if you stepped out of line you would be enslaved or thrown into the arena full of gladiators for the crowd's pleasure. The Romans ruled our land through force. There was no give and take; they ruled you obeyed. Some may disagree with this and say they were more like pleasant landowners bringing us culture and civilisation. I say you only have to look at their roads to see how considerate and caring the conquerors were. England is transversed by Roman roads and they are invariably straight. They went where they liked, when they liked and if you got in their way you were in big trouble, just ask Boadicea, Queen of the Iceni Britons, who was slaughtered by them. However, she did take an exacting toll for their intrusion before her downfall. Some say they allowed her to take poison, but I doubt it, she was probably thrown to the lions in one of the many gladiatorial rings that they had in London. Now, take the usual English roads, they twist and turn, snaking around peoples' lands and borders. This is a 'give and take' road system; it is twice as long but far more amenable to the local population and I am sure this reflects in our attitude. OK, so this is a simplistic example, but you get the general idea.

At the end of our trek, we arrived at a small bench that overlooked great swathes of Sussex countryside. The county town of Lewes looked like a toy village on a children's television programme. It was time to sit and soakup the glorious day. Huge white cumulus clouds drifted like great sailing ships across the blue sky, their grey bottoms heavy with rain that had yet to fall. They threw giant shadows across the flat lands below, pushed by a warm south westerly that had come from the Spanish coast way over the horizon. A thousand assorted greens were lying across the landscape in patches and shades that only an artist could capture with paint or a perhaps a poet with words. It was only a stone's throw from here that one of the turning points in British history took place, The Battle of Lewes.

This was a battle between Simon de Montfort and Henry 111(King John's son) in 1264. De Montfort wanted the kingdom ruled more by the people than the Crown. After the battle, while he still held Henry prisoner (good bargaining point) he formed our first proper Parliament or talking place. For the first time he not only included Knights and Barons but also all other classes of society, only excluding thieves and peasants. It did not help de Montfort much as they all still quarrelled and within a short time Henry's son, Prince Edward, killed de Montfort at The Battle of Evesham. However, he left us a legacy that stands today and it all came about on a little hill near Lewes. On a more unpleasant note they say that the bleached bones of the dead were so prolific from the battle that they could still be seen amongst the fields and hedgerows nearly a century later.

All that is ancient history now, long forgotten, the fields hold their secrets and the countryside is at peace. At this point on Mount Caburn, with high summer in the British countryside, sitting on the edge of paradise, overlooking mankind, you feel almost immortal. You would be inclined to think that things could not get any better, however you would be wrong.

I removed my rucksack and like a magician pulling a rabbit from his hat I reached in and pulled out something that would make a hungry person give you his soul, a large Marks and Spencer's non-stick frying pan, followed by a complete breakfast. With butcher's best sausages and prime back bacon.

Before too long it was all sizzling. The tomatoes were simmering in the pan with the sausages browning and bacon curling up its crisp edges. The sweet smell of wild grasses was temporarily replaced with an even sweeter smell of a fry-up. I had converted the ancient hill fort into The Greasy Spoon Café. Mind you the one thing guaranteed to put a smile on Yana's face, is a cooked breakfast, anytime, anywhere. We were like greedy pigs in a truffle patch, chomping away at our feast. Rolly was tucking into one of the sausages with a satisfied look on her little doggy face.

'Ah', the pure pleasure that good food and the company of God's creatures brings, so simple and yet so perfect. A thermos of hot tea washed the breakfast down and we sat in silence watching the World go by.

What a pilgrimage, some may have to go to Canterbury Cathedral to touch Becket's bones, but give me good company and a full belly any day. We are all much like that if we would only admit it; we make our world so complex and forget the basics, simple pleasures that reach down into the depths of our souls.

As we packed up to leave I was left wondering if Yana was going to expect a fry-up on the top of Mount Caburn every time we came. Still, I could think of worse things to do on a Sunday morning.

*Alpaca's looking quite at home in a Sussex meadow*

*Breakfast on Mount Carburn near Lewes. It is a long walk but the majestic views are well worth it.*

*The local sheep checking out the dog as we walked past. These are part of the famous John Ellman lamb stock.*

# JESSIE'S STORY

'What Jessie'? I sparked up in total amazement, 'you have been sewing for over 72 years?', I was in Jessie's flat, a small apartment in Buxted, East Sussex. Jessie was my favourite type of customer, cheerful and chatty, full of positive energy. Her enthusiasm belied her 80 years of life, although it was only 8 a.m. she was on top form.

'Yes, I started sewing when I was eight years old and now I am 80, not a bad record is that'.

'Did your mum teach you how to sew originally'? I questioned Jessie, hoping for a story and out it came. Jessie did not disappoint. It was like removing the lid off a bottle of fizz, out spurted the wonderful story of her life.

Jessie had spent the first few years of her life growing up with her elder sisters, Millie and Ethel and her younger brother, in a flat in Cannonbury Street, Islington, North London. Although by the time Jessie was six, they had moved to Downham, in Bromley. Jessie's first experience of sewing came early, she clearly remembers her mother teaching her how to make the cotton nappies for her younger brother on an old Singer treadle machine that had been left to her mum by granny. Jessie was also taught how to sew at school and they made their own drill slips, but no school uniform. In truth very few parents in the 1930's had the money for school uniforms, so as not to embarrass the children that could not afford them, the school had no rules as to what you could wear, although they did insist on shoes, however patched up.

By 1937, at the age of 14, Jessie's mum, Amelia, had already booked her place of work. Jessie left school and started work at Badcocks, in Goswell Road, near The Angel, in North London. Both her older sisters sewed at the factory so she had no problem getting a job there. It was quite a trek from their Bromley home each day. The six o'clock train to London, then the tube, tram and finally the bus to work, arriving before 7.30 each morning, six days a week. Jessie had a three-month training period before they would let her near a sewing machine, but before too long she was sitting with her sisters in a long line of machines and machinists. Everything made was paid piecework and you had to work hard and fast for your money. No mistakes, mind you, or they were docked from your wages, double the price of the normal work. The sewing machines were all in rows, as they were turned by a single huge shaft, that ran the entire length of the sewing room. If your belt broke you would have to wait for the maintenance man to come and repair it. However, time was money and the girls soon learnt a trick or two with their hair pins; they would sit under the machine with the shaft whizzing away and pierce holes in the broken belt, then with utmost care use a bent hair clip to mend the belt and swing it back onto the shaft. Hey presto, they were back in action and earning money.

On Jessie's first day as a proper machinist her machine broke. Desperate to earn her money and with no spare machine available, she took her sewing all the way back home to Bromley with her. Jessie spent the whole weekend sewing on her mother's Singer treadle machine. On Monday she took all the work in and found she had earned half-a-crown, not even enough for the train ride home. It was a hard lesson to learn, but with piecework speed was everything. Every day Jessie and her two sisters would make their way to work until one day war broke out. Jessie and her sisters still sewed all day at Badcocks but now they were making very different items of clothing indeed. They had gone from children's coats, leggings, hats and posh dresses, to underpants for soldiers. You would not think of it really, but the army needed tens of thousands of pairs of underpants and Jessie made them in all shapes and sizes; it would always bring a few laughs when the extra large pairs were sewn up, as the machinists would all wear them on their heads as they sewed.

On more than one occasion bombs had taken out the railway or the tram and getting to work was becoming a nightmare; getting across war torn London was just not possible. Eventually Jessie and her sisters managed to get work closer to home. Jessie started in a local shop but hated working there. She missed all the chat and action from the factory so she kept her eyes peeled and soon found work in another factory.

By the early 1940's Jessie had fallen in love with her future husband George. The wedding was all arranged for June 1944, but George who was in the Para's, was suddenly called away. The invasion of Europe was planned on their wedding day and unfortunately that took precedence over their wedding. While an enormous armada was landing on the beaches of Normandy, George was dropped into action in North Africa. However by

August, with a short break in fighting George was allowed a one week compassionate leave to get married and have his honeymoon. He had no idea what Lord Montgomery and the War Office had in store for him.

George and Jessie managed to get most of the family together for a hasty, but happy wedding before George was rushed away again. In September he was dropped into a fierce battle at Arnhem where the allies were trying to push too hard, too far, too soon. Montgomery, eager for a quick end to the war and to grab as much territory as possible had underestimated the German fighting machine. George was dropped with 8000 other Para's just short of the small town of Arnhem, made famous later in the epic war film, A Bridge Too Far. The fighting was so fierce and deadly that within a few days, less than 2000 of George's paras were still alive; it was a massacre. George was one of the lucky survivors, but was captured by the Germans and shipped off to a prisoner of war camp. Here, George spent the last year of the war until American soldiers overran the prison camp and freed the men. All this time Jessie was waiting patiently for word of George at home, but it was not until 1946 that George and Jessie finally started their married life together.

After the war and George's homecoming, and the bunting and street parties had finally ended, the real hardships of the post-war shortages had begun. Jessie had to get back to work to earn a living and help support her growing family. She found work at Triang Toys in Croydon making pram covers. Triang were part of Petigrew Prams-which was very useful as she managed to get a pram at a discount for her first born. Later on, the Triang and Petigrew factories, were taken over by Sleepeazy beds. Jessie worked for another 14 years at Sleepeazy in Murston, Redhill, making covers for the mattresses. When Jessie retired she was the line manager of 25 sewing girls and knew just about everything anyone could ever know about her trade.

By 1983 Jessie had spent 46 years in the sewing industry, she had seen a world where the horse was king of the road and a London tram was a common method of transport, change to one with microwaves and computers; still the sewing machine had survived all the changes that the new world could throw at it. Although Jessie retired from the busy life of factory sewing, she still sews to this day. I spent a lovely hour or so, listening to her life as I placed a new gear in her 1966 Singer 447.

'OK Jessie', I said with a satisfied grin on my face, like a fat priest who has just feasted to his fill and was happily rubbing his belly, 'I now believe you have been sewing for 72 years, may the next 72 be just as interesting'. We both laughed, I left her small apartment that was full of old pictures and memories, with Jessie as happy as a lark.

The machine was purring away, and Jessie was bent over her sewing machine, just like she has been doing for over two thirds of a century. I had the wonderful pleasure of listening to Jessie's life, retold by the person who as a young woman had climbed over the bomb blasted rubble of the London streets, making her way to work. The same woman that had sat, knitting patiently, waiting for any word of her husband in 1945. For a brief few moments I had seen life through Jessie's eyes and travelled on a magical mystery tour of forgotten factories and long ago places.

Thank you Jessie, it was a great privilege.

*Cricket on the green at Eastbourne College. A British scene that has not changed much since Victorian times.*

*Dawn on the seafront when the sea was like a mill pond. Sometimes it is so wild that the waves crash down with such force that the ground shakes*

*Beachy Head - a one way trip if you slip. The famous red and white lighthouse at the base of the cliffs - some 500 feet below. Built at the turn of the 20th century to warn ships of the dangerous rocks*

*The Stone Cross windmill which is now surrounded by new houses, she still looks beautiful in the sunlight*

# ONE OF THOSE DAYS

It was going to be one of 'those' days again. I had just popped in to the new toilets at Langney Point to answer the call of nature.

'You'll 'ave to wait, I ain't finished yet' a short round woman said to me. Not the sort of thing you expect to hear when entering the men's loos. She had a wet mop in her hand and looked like the sort of person that you would not argue with.

'Hang on a mo', she added seeing the woeful look in my eyes that comes from one cup of tea too many.

'You can use one of the stalls, I've finished them, and don't make a mess'. I squeezed past the big, burly cleaner and made for the kiosk. No sooner than I had shut the door and made doubly sure it was locked properly than she shouted to me, 'I don't mind watching the old man pee but I ain't watchin you'. I realised that I was going to have a running commentary during my short stop. As soon as I could, I tried to make my escape. She, in the meantime had lit up a 'ciggie' and was leaning on the entrance door waiting for me to leave. She looked like an overweight call girl on a slow afternoon. I quickly washed up under her watchful gaze, trying to figure out the new vandal proof sinks that have automatic soap, water and drying all in one hole.

'Ere, May, I got a man in 'ere I 'ave', she shouted to her friend who was cleaning the other loo next door.

'Don't wear 'im out, leave something for me you old cow' came the reply. They were both laughing as I made my escape. Typical, just a quick stop and I am being abused again.

'You ain't made a mess 'ave yer', she shouted after me as I made a quick step to the car, by now they were both out the front of the loos having a good laugh at my expense.

'Are you sure you have not touched this light unit'? I asked the old girl at my next call.

'Well, I might have, just the once'.

I had to act like a detective and discover why the fuse kept blowing on her French Singer. The call had started badly as she was partially deaf and her phone had a problem. I had knocked on number 42, after no reply assumed that she was out, annoyed, I phoned her. To my surprise she answered. 'Hi,

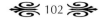

its Alex here, I have come to fix your machine but you are not answering the door'.

'The door is open', came the reply. That's funny, I am standing outside and it does not look open to me.

'What number are you'?

'42', came the reply.

'I am standing outside 42, are you sure it is 42'?

'Yes in the cul-de-sac, number 42'.

Well, I am not in a cul-de-sac, I am in a normal road. I drove up the road to the cul-de-sac and sure enough, waving out the window of number 32, like a frantic aged Rapunzel, was the old dear.

'I am so sorry you had trouble finding me, it is this blessed phone distorting my voice, water on the line they told me'.

I was not convinced, the scatty old girl looked like she was definitely not all there. Her hair was in tangles, her clothes a mess, she had buttoned the front of her cardigan up twisted; she looked like she had been through a washing machine. As I was getting down to work I found little bits of cut up plaster stuck all over the light unit of the machine. Each screw had a small plaster stuck over it, 'strange', I thought. That is when I started to interrogate the customer. Of course in true British spy mode she denied everything, whether she had just forgotten or not, well, who can guess. I dared not plug anything in until I was sure that I would not get electrocuted. Slowly but surely she was buckled under my persistent questioning and the true story unfolded. She had bought a new light bulb that would not fit into her machine, so in good old 'do it yourself' mode, she had taken the light fitting off the machine and then proceeded to take it apart. Where the sprung brass clips for the light were, she had put them back in upside down, touching each other, live to neutral, and used a plaster to stick it all together. A near perfect death trap!!! Needless to say each time she tried to plug the machine in, the fuse blew.

As I was fixing her handiwork she went and made me a cup of coffee I so desperately needed. I should have guessed that things were not going to get any better. She came back into the room and placed a lovely looking cup of coffee on a small table in the centre of the room. Then there was a ring on the phone followed by a re-enactment of my problem, trying to find her, but this time with the telephone engineer. She was shouting instructions down the line at him, I could just imagine his face. While she was occupied, I took advantage of the coffee, little did I know the old girl had heated it in her new microwave for far too long; it was a smouldering volcano. I took one sip and the scolding hot liquid burnt my lips then my tongue. I wanted to spit it out, but I was in her living room so I ran, sucking air into my mouth, to the kitchen sink. She was oblivious to all this, hanging out her beloved window waving to the British Telecom engineer. I recovered with some cold water from the tap and returned to the sewing machine. She saw me coming in and realized what had happened.

'Have I overcooked your coffee', she said apologetically.

'I'll be alright', I replied through my burnt lips.

'I only got the microwave last week and am still experimenting on it'.

I just smiled back. 'Preferably not on me next time', I thought as I got down to work.

Things did not get any better. The BT man found his plug socket was right by the sewing machine. The whole table and tools had to be shifted so that he could get to the area and I was left trying to fix the machine with tools scattered around the room. Then entered the fourth player in our little pantomime, Whiskey, the cat.

'Ah there is my baby', she said cuddling the black and white cat as if it was the prodigal son returning home.

'I have your fish already for you, I just have to cook it'. She turned to me, still cuddling the cat. 'I cannot understand it, he ran away yesterday morning, hardly touching his fish and I have not seen him since'.

Well, I thought, no surprise to me at all. She put Whiskey lovingly down on the settee, stroked him and then went to cook his breakfast. In the mean time I had sorted her electrics so she was not going to kill herself, and finished off servicing the machine. Little did I know that the microwave was the cause of her disappearing cat as well as my scalded lips.

Things were about to get worse; I was sitting at the machine, concentrating on balancing the tension. The BT engineer was taking his first sip of coffee at the same time as the hungry cat was sniffing the plate of micro- waved fish. Unable to resist his hunger, the cat grabbed a mouthful of fish, squeals, hisses and darts across the room. The BT engineer spat his volcanic lava clear across the room and all over my toolbox, the nutty old dear walked in just in time to see her cat disappear out of the door again.

'Oh I don't know why this always happens to me', she said hands in the air, treading the piece of fish that the cat had dropped, into the carpet. Meanwhile, the BT engineer was doing a rather impressive impersonation of a Red Indian tribal dance, around the living room table, flapping his hand in front of his face and hopping up and down. I was sniggering, knowing just how he felt and wondering who was going to clear up the mess. Normally, you would have to pay good money to see such a farce that only Oscar Wilde could dream up, but I had a front row seat for free.

Things eventually calmed down. I cleaned up my toolbox and scraped most of the squashed fish off the floor. The BT engineer had left in a hurry to get something from the depot; at least I think that is what he said I could not understand him too well as his speech was slurred.

'I think I had better give you a lesson on how to use your new microwave', I said to my customer, guiding her into the kitchen. After a few minutes and a couple of trial runs heating up cups of water, she got the hang of it. I left her leaning out of her favourite window shouting for her cat that was nowhere to be seen and would never touch fish again.

I often wonder how they survive so well, these scatty old girls, I don't know if it is an English trait but I meet them as regular as clockwork. Their husbands have invariably 'dropped off their twig' years ago and they have managed perfectly well without them, leaving a trail of destruction in their wake.

Back at home, sometime later, I was standing in front of the mirror gently rubbing Vaseline onto my sore lips. I could not help wondering how many lives that cat had used up in the last week and if it would ever take the risk of returning to his scatty owner who was probably still leaning out of her window calling for him.

*I am smiling because Yana is telling me to pull my belly in so that the pretty Firle church is visible under my arm.*

*A typical country lane leading down into the Sussex woodland. I travel these roads every week*

*A simply beautiful scene near Wilmington, the white horses appeared as the mist cleared*

*They say this strange carved wooden figurehead was from a shipwreck. The Dutch ship had been caught in a storm off Cuckmere Haven a long time ago. It is now on a pub wall in Alfriston.*

# LEWES

'What a day', I was thinking as the mobile phone rang again, the third time in less than 10 minutes. I pulled over onto the verge just above The Cuckmere Valley and listened to another customer who wanted their machine done today.... Right now!!!!

I gazed across the beautiful valley beneath me and watched the river lazily make its way down to the sea. Ah, to be a fish or a seagull or just any of God's creatures that could not answer the phone. I realised the customer on the other end of the line had stopped talking and I quickly spurted out my favourite line, 'I will get to you presently Mrs Janes', that was my stock answer to when I was arriving. Did I have three pairs of hands? No, just the one pair. Did my car fly? Not to my knowledge, it just followed all the other cars; so there was no way I was going to get to her any quicker however many times she phoned. I hung up and let the beauty of the scenery calm me down before heading on my way to Newhaven. I made a quick stop at a luggage factory to drop off some needles, then another at the Newhaven Bus Depot to repair their upholstery Toyota, an industrial walking foot machine. They were not too happy as one of their drivers had got drunk the night before and did not show up for work. Then, off to old George Sinclair, in Lewes. He has a soft furnishing business just off Cliff High Street.

Lewes has to be one of my favourite towns in the whole world; it has more of a mix of architecture and history than any place I have ever seen. From ancient to modern; even before our knowledge of history began, Lewes (meaning hill fort) had been home to dinosaurs, with their teeth still being found in the soil. Then Neolithic man, who around 8,000 BC started clearing the Downland for farming, leaving the beautiful landscape much as we see it today, their ancient mystic burial mounds still dot the high places of the soft hills. One has to remember that it was only around 5,000 BC that the sea filled the area between Britain and Europe making us a fortress island. That is when invasions from the continent started, we had Celts arriving from Europe, bringing their blonde hair and blue eyes; then around 55BC the most famous of Roman rulers, Julius Caesar, decided to bring some men across the Channel to our country and give us grief; I seem to remember that it was he who made the wonderful, brief statement to the Senate, when describing his adventures in Britain, veni, vidi, vici -

I came, I saw, I conquered', the show off; he said it again when he invaded Egypt and met the dazzling 18 year old Cleopatra. But it was Cleopatra who had really conquered Caesar's heart, mind you it was not until AD43 years after Caesar's death that Claudius sent a proper force of over 40,000 soldiers to our shores with orders to quell the rebellious Brits. Many say that they landed near Lewes and there is proof that the hill top fort at Mount Caburn suffered a huge fire at this time. It only takes a bit of guesswork to see that the ideal landing spot for an invading army from Boulogne in France was the port of Lewes. It would have been an ominous and terrible sight to see invaders coming up the River Ouse in such numbers and know there was no escape.

After a quiet lull and Roman rule, invaders started turning up from just about everywhere, Angles, Jutes and Saxons from Denmark, France and Germany. Later the Vikings started on us; it was as if we had become the main shopping centre of Europe where everyone had to visit; you know what people say, 'The grass is always greener', mind you in the case of Britain it usually was. Then in 1066, it was the turn of the Normans, it was at this time the impressive Lewes Castle was built along with Lewes Priory, which became the home of William the Conqueror's trusted Knight, William de Warenne and his wife, Gundrada, who was possibly William the Conqueror's daughter, though that is still a hot potato amongst historians.

In the 1840's, when the main railway was being built through Lewes, it went through the old Priory on its way to Brighton. As the foundations for the railway sleepers were dug, the remains of Warenne and his wife Gundrada were discovered laying in their lead coffins, undisturbed for centuries. It was an amazing find.

The architecture in Lewes is second to none. As well as the mass of ancient stone work, there are beautiful Tudor oak beamed houses, like Anne of Cleves House (One of Henry V111's, six wives) and Georgian and Regency town houses. Lewes has the impressive County Law Courts and countless other wonderful places. The flint buildings, well, not just flint but all kinds, normal sea flint, Downland flint, knapped flint and the hardest of all, square napped flint. A house built of square shaped-knapped flint, is a work of art, to knap a flint into a square is very difficult, but there were a few skilled tradesmen from the olden days that

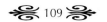

knew how to do it. The result is a flat faced polished wall rather than the knobbly normal flint wall, and what a sight they make when the sun catches the side of the buildings.

Lewes is so steeped in history that you could easily spend a lifetime just studying the town, even then, you would probably only scratch the surface. On the darker side was our queen, Mary Tudor, better know as 'Bloody Mary'. During her short reign she tried to convert the country from its growing Protestant population back to Catholicism. To do this she used extreme methods and anyone refusing to renounce their Protestant faith would be tortured and killed. Just above Lewes on a hillside there is a monument to seventeen of the unlucky ones who met their gruesome end outside The Star Inn. The monument reads as follows.

*In loving memory of the under named*
*Seventeen protestant martyrs*
*Who, for their faithful testimony to*
*God's truth were, during the reign of*
*Queen Mary, burnt to death in front*
*Of the Star Inn, now the Town Hall-Lewes.*

It is a chilling reminder of the power that the Royal Family used to wield. One of the most famous of our sayings from this dreadful period came from the Bishop of Oxford as he waited his turn to be burned alive, 'We shall this day light such a candle by God's grace in England, as I trust, shall never be put out'. Luckily for England within five years Bloody Mary had died. She died aged 42 in extreme pain, some say as penance for her wicked ways. After her death the whole of England celebrated, and one of our most brilliant rulers came to the throne, Queen Elizabeth, later to be known as 'Good Queen Bess': Mind you, probably not by her sister Mary Queen of Scots whose head she kindly removed.

So as you see, our county town of Lewes holds a special place in our little corner of England and a place in my heart. I would say that, if Lewes were to sink into the soil, England would have lost a treasure more precious than any crown. A trip to Lewes is a journey through the history of our country, from the Dinosaur to Deep Pan Pizza. No wonder Daniel Defoe once described Lewes as one of the most romantic towns he had ever laid his eyes upon. Lewes has just about everything.... except decent parking.

After a couple of easy repairs at George's soft furnishing business, I headed for my most important call of the day, Harveys Brewery. No not to fix any machines, but to stock-up on their lovely traditional ales. 'Ah' the smell of Harvey's malt and hops wafting in the breeze guides you to their factory right in the High Street.

Around 1790 John Harvey finished his fine brewery at Bridge Wharf in Lewes. The brewery still dominates the scene and air, from its riverside position. It is an interesting Gothic building that is pleasing to the eye and interesting to walk around. The impressive building has stored within its old walls the secret art of true brewing. I can honestly say that to my mind Harveys make one of the most excellent selections of fine ales in the land. More than once I have enjoyed the intoxicating elixir that slips down the throat as sweet as any of Pan's melodious grape. Harveys, still a family business, have over a dozen different ales to suit all pallets, from dry and rich, to sweet and soft. My personal favourite is the gold award winning 'Sussex Sweet'. A dark and yeasty rich ale full of Sussex hops and spring water; mixed as only Harveys can, then aged in the Georgian fermenting vats to a superb texture and flavour.

I stocked up with a dozen bottles of their 'falling over juice' and headed back to the car. That would be enough ale to see me through as I knew it would be another month before I would have more calls in the Lewes area and another good reason to visit Harveys once more.

Lewes is also famous for its amazing bonfire spectaculars that celebrate the failure of The Gun Powder Plot in 1605. It was an attempt to blow up The Houses of Parliament by Guy Fawkes and his team. Fawkes was executed in the most horrible manner possible. He was hung till near death, then drawn and quartered. Nasty. Each year to celebrate his failure, (just an excuse really) Lewes holds the annual November 5th bonfire celebrations. It is also to remember the martyrs who died for their religious beliefs some 50 years prior to the Gunpowder Plot. Bonfire night in Lewes is an amazing spectacle with burning barrels rolling down the streets and thousands of marchers parading in old Elizabethan dress, holding poles and flaming torches. Each year up to 60,000 people attend the celebrations. It is always a busy time for me as many of the costume makers get to fever pitch in the weeks prior to the event and the machines fail under the pressure; that's when I get the emergency phone calls at midnight, thank God for answerphones.

By midday, with the sun at its zenith and with the shadows stolen from the buildings, I pointed the Land Rover east and headed for home. The drive was more pleasant than earlier for I had switched the mobile phone off and was enjoying the beautiful Sussex countryside while the road led me back to Eastbourne and my lunch.

Rolly greeted me enthusiastically as I drove in, but soon went off to sniff the mud flaps on the car to smell where I had been all morning. After a quick sandwich for lunch I carried on with a few machines that customers had dropped off, finished the computer work that had built up, and spent the superb summer evening with the family.

How satisfying, a good meal, good company and a bottle of Harveys finest ale can be; it almost makes working for a living worthwhile, mind you that is a big emphasis on the 'almost'. I had left Mrs Janes until the last call of the day, just to get my own back for annoying me on my way to the first call of the morning. Well I did tell her I would be calling 'presently'.

*The impressive gate house leading to the castle in Lewes. A thousand years ago Norman soldiers would have marched along the cobbled streets through the gate, every day.*

*The top of Lewes Castle, the small castle is still impressive standing proud above Lewes*

*Harveys Brewery, one of my favourite places in Lewes, a busy little brewery*

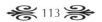

# HOLIDAY FROM HELL

There was a strange smell at the farm I had just called on, something vaguely familiar, but distant. I could not put my finger on it as I started work on a battered, old Italian Necchi, then as I removed the needle plate for inspection it all came flooding back. It reminded me of our 'holiday from hell'.

As the days of the year rolled away we realised we had not booked a holiday and knew from experience that working straight through the year without a break was not good for the soul. To make it worse Eastbourne was in full tourist swing. The Red Arrows were doing their spectacular aerial display above the seafront, leaving trails of multicoloured fumes covering the eager crowds. I carried on with my calls dodging around the traffic, using all the back roads that I knew so well and most holidaymakers never knew existed.

Each day as many as a 100,000 extra tourists poured onto the beaches to lap up the summer weather. Eastbourne in high tourist season is a sight to behold, a spectacle in itself, gardens and beaches deserted for the winter months become crowded with lobster red holidaymakers. The mess that is left from up to half a million visitors in the four peak days of Eastbourne Airbourne is extraordinary. My early morning stroll along the promenade is like walking through a field that a band of gypsies have just deserted, there is mess everywhere. It is a logistical masterpiece by the council to organise and clean up after the event. I wonder how long it will go on, before they use some excuse to call it to a halt. Many of the holidaymakers from the North of England have a do or die, attitude to getting a tan. A tan at all costs. I suppose they think that the holiday will last a little longer if they have their tan to wear for an extra month or so. The trade union hotel is normally fully booked with eager northerners enjoying their seaside break; many of the back roads become blocked with the hundreds of coaches that pick-up and deliver our visitors. These great land whales with bellies full of luggage load and unload all day long endlessly dropping and filling up with visitors.

After a while, seeing everyone else enjoying themselves, it got to me and I seriously needed a break. I decided that as soon as I arrived home we would book a holiday and take a few days well-needed rest from work.

Yana and I sat down that night, with a glass of wine and looked through all the usual holiday brochures. We decided a nice trip down to Cornwall would be just what the doctor ordered; and on the way back we could visit The Great Singer Mausoleum in Paignton, a place I always wanted to see. Thoughts of strolls across the moors and Cornish ice cream were enough to convince me and we were soon phoning up for a holiday cottage to rent. As the evening drew on, no vacancies could be found at all; we had left it way too late in the year and became desperate. We phoned the brochure company and asked them to tell us what they had available, instead of us choosing a nice looking cottage, only to find it was booked. Half-an-hour later the phone rang and a polite voice on the other end told me they had two cottages still available. Two out of two hundred, no wonder we could not find anything still available. Alarm bells should have started ringing straight away but the bottle of wine was nearly empty and we were in holiday mode. I had to make a decision and with only two left, time was running out. For one cottage it was necessary to leave the car a mile away. That sounded like hard work and the other was on a working milk farm. Well, a working milk farm sounded quite charming.

It was now well into the night but we were as excited as a honeymoon couple. We looked up our little farm on the map and in the dim light opened it out over the dining room table; it was such a picturesque spot, just on the edge of Dartmoor National Park with its open moorland and scenic views. We toasted our holiday and went to bed, happy that we had managed to book a break. With pleasant thoughts of strolling around wonderful forests and the moors I drifted into a happy sleep. Little did I know, we had just booked up the 'holiday-from-hell'.

The holiday started badly. As we left home late we soon found out that we had decided to travel on the busiest day of the year, the first Saturday following the end of the summer school term. A trip that would normally take five hours was taking all day at five miles an hour. By late afternoon in a hot car we stopped for some food. We found a nice fish'n'chip shop that served, lovely battered cod and a bag full of piping hot chips for a reasonable price. I smothered my chips in salt and vinegar and we sat on the busy roadside chomping away at our simple feast. Another three hours in the car and we split off from the main Atlantic Highway, towards our farm. By now evening was drawing on and after the usual heated arguments over map reading we stumbled, more by luck than judgement, on the small lane down to our farm. It was a single track, very narrow with the hedgerows almost touching both sides of the Land Rover. It led to only one place, our holiday home. We were really excited as the narrow lane led down into thick forests. After about two miles we reached our farm. It was a mind-blowing shock!!!

I had been to many working farms on my travels, but none like this. It was in a hollow and the disappearing sun left long shadows over the farm giving it an eerie appearance. The yard was covered in the stuff that cows like to leave all over the fields, but had left it all over the farmyard instead. I looked for a dry patch where I could park the car and get the family out without getting covered in the muck. Just outside our cottage was a slight rise and patch of green. I drove the Land Rover onto the lump of grass. I told the kids not to move as I surveyed the area. Our cottage was pushed up to the side of a hill with no view except the cut out embankment. To the front, the view was of the farm itself, which was not too comforting. The smell as I got out of the car was suffocating, a thick pungent stink of warm muck and animals. There were flies everywhere, they came and hovered over the car like a black swarm over a dead camel. As the rest of the family gingerly exited the car, the flies decided that we were their next target. Obviously more interesting than the dung they had been sitting on all day.

I was swishing the flies away when farmer Ron came out to greet us. He was talking some strange gibberish and as hard as I tried, I could not understand his thick Cornish accent. After a few minutes of smiling at him and nodding vainly something strange started to happen. My mind, like all minds (a wonderful piece of evolved equipment, that I make no bones about trying to understand), started to decipher Ron's words. Slowly he made sense. His words were coming into focus like someone putting on a pair of glasses after struggling to read their newspaper. He was asking me if I had a pleasant trip and smiling at me with his one good tooth. Ron kindly took us on a tour of the cottage, a converted milking shed that left a lot to be desired. We were tired and hungry and as soon as Ron had left, Yana and I looked at each other. We had made a big mistake, but I was exhausted from driving all day and was in no mood to travel home.

We decided to have something to eat and get a good-night's rest, things often look a bit rosier in the morning after a good kip, that was a laugh, but I was jumping ahead. Unloading the car Tom's football rolled out of the boot and we watched in horror as the white leather rotated into a brown stinking blob. 'Leave it Tom, we can clean it up tomorrow', I quickly shouted as he made a run for his ball.

Tom stopped and looked longingly at his beloved football, then shrugged. At that point a brown mess on four legs ran towards us, it was the farmer's dog. It was like a brown, moving, matted carpet of muck with bright eyes that looked up at us appealingly. I am sure it was unaware of its state and wanted to play; we wanted to escape from it as soon as we could.

'Her name is Tess' shouted Ron from across the yard 'Jus' kick it up the arse if she gets to be a pest'. I waved to Ron and wondered what we had let ourselves in for.

The dog followed us into the back door and left muddy, dirty paw prints all over the kitchen floor. I threw a biscuit out of the door and quickly closed it behind the mutt.

Dinner was a disaster. Sarah burnt her hand while pulling the pizza out of the oven; she promptly dropped our supper on the floor. We looked down sorrowfully at our food, no one was going to eat anything that had been on that floor; it was way too filthy. I opened the door and called Tess, our muck covered sheepdog. She pounded in and gratefully slunk out the back door with her prize, like a hyena with a pup. I saw her nip off into the fields above the cottage to enjoy her unexpected feast; while she was a happy dog we were going hungry for the night.

Flies were everywhere by the million At first we kept the doors and windows closed but the mouldy smell inside the cottage made it impossible to breathe. We just had to put up with the flies that circled endlessly around the lights and turned the lampshades into grubby brown-rimmed glowing blobs. A headache was on top of me, you know the sort, a pounding, throbbing pain that blurs the vision and makes you feel queasy. I sat in the living room wondering what we had done to deserve this, it was supposed to be our holiday, not a trip to Hell, and we had paid for the privilege. I turned on the TV to get the ten o'clock news only to find the television fuzzed and the screen jumped like something out of a 1960's house. It was probably due to the poor reception, or maybe it really was 40 years old. I popped some headache pills, looked bleary eyed at my family who were putting a brave face on things despite the disaster, and announced I was going to bed.

Well, I thought I was. The bed was obviously acquired from the former leader of the Spanish Inquisition, as it was far closer to a dungeon rack than a bed. It had lengths of wire running horizontally across the frame and a two-inch hair filled mattress. I laid in pain, shifting from one side to another and drifted into a painful and restless sleep.

At 4.30 am, noise, noise, noise. A herd of buffalo, disguised as cows were storming down the drive; they had come from the high pastures and were clattering towards the milking sheds opposite our cottage. The noise was unbearable, it broke the quiet morning hush of the countryside like a traffic accident. I tried to stand up properly but the wires that had worked on my back during the night had crippled me. I walked like a painful version of Quasimodo, the hunchback, towards the kettle. I woke Yana and told her we needed to escape. With the kids in the car we headed out for the day and a place to have breakfast. After a good meal, some hot coffee and fresh air, the Cornish countryside started to work its magical charm on me.

'Lets go sightseeing for the day', I proposed to the family, they all agreed as staying in the cottage was not a viable alternative.

We spent eleven hours driving around the Cornish coast to Lands End, the western most tip of England and then around the Moors. By the time we headed back to farmer Ron's, it was nearing suppertime. We had that in a heated bag from the takeaway in the nearest town. After supper I decided we should investigate the local woods we were staying in the middle of, we set off to explore the nearest path. Ron came trotting up the side of the cottage, all knobbly-kneed and wobbly, like a kid with his shorts round his ankles. 'Orf out are we'? He said inquiringly, with a hopeful gleam in his eye. 'We thought we would just pop into the woods for a stroll', I replied. 'I'll cum with thee then', Ron replied, 'Hang on a jiffy'. He trotted back to his farm and appeared with a rifle. I was not amused; I looked at Yana and shrugged.

Ron took us deep into the woods and all was quiet, too quiet, no birds, no animals, the whole area seemed to be dead. Then we came upon a lake but that too, was stagnant with a blue scum floating around the edges. Many of the trees seemed to be half dead and the branches twisted like a witches' knuckles with little or no leaves. It was weird. 'I don't like the look of these woods, everything seems to be dead or dying', I whispered to Yana as we walked behind Ron who had his rifle cocked over his arm.

'Come on, come on', Ron beckoned toward us waving his arm, 'Keep up'. It suddenly dawned on me that the 'old bugger' was taking us out into the woods to shoot us. Why else would we be walking so far as it was getting dark? It was all starting to make sense, no one in his or her right mind would stay in a cottage like ours, it was all a ploy. You get the rich town folk out into hillbilly land, then take all their stuff, strip the car down for parts, sell off the camera and any clothes to his relatives who probably lived next door, and they would disappear forever. No one ever complained, as no one ever got out of the farm alive.

Just when I was getting really worried and my finely tuned paranoid brain was getting to overload point, Ron called me over.

'Jus over there is an old shop that used to be 'ere in these woods, go 'ave a look, go on jus over there behind them trees'.

Now I was really worried, here he was, asking me to go off into the woods to see a shop. What was a shop doing in the middle of the woods, how stupid did he think I was? Mind you, I was doing just what he wanted, so who was the stupid one? I slowly moved towards the trees where Ron was pointing with his rifle, I could not see anything.

'Over to yer right a bit' Ron shouted, sure enough, there were a few bricks, the perfect place to shoot me I was thinking, no one would ever find my body. This was it, my last few seconds of life and to make things worse I had paid this old devil for the pleasure.

To my surprise, Ron beckoned me back, a ray of hope shone through; maybe I was going to live (long enough to get a refund from that bloody holiday cottage agent anyway).

'Used to be the old mining shop for the arsenic mines over the hill. Want to see them? Largest arsenic and copper mines in the world, for a while they was'.

'Arsenic mines'? I answered incredulously.

'Ar that will be right, best arsenic you could buy, two drops would kill a goat. Fancy 'avin a shot with 'ers rifle while its still light'? Ron said holding up the rifle and fumbling in his baggy trousers for some bullets. Now he was talking my kind of music. For twenty minutes we emptied his rifle into the forest shooting cans off branches and twigs, Yana turned out to be the best shot out of the lot of us with Tom a close second. I was still a bit shaky from my brush with death earlier and my shots went a bit wild; one hit a stone and something squawked off into the forest. Then Ron took us to the huge abandoned copper mine where they still had the special ovens for converting the copper sulphate into arsenic.

'Don't breathe too 'ard in there boy or you'll be 'avin a sore throat for a month', said Ron as I peeked inside. The acrid smell of death was everywhere. The mines had been closed for decades and left to ruin. There was nothing anyone could do, and it would be almost impossible to reclaim the land as it was poisoned forever. We stood on a small crop of high land, overlooking the mines, even in the soft glow of the summer evening that can make the hardest of buildings or towns soften, it was a desolate place. In the middle of what should have been beautiful woodland we witnessed a scene straight from Hell itself. Now it all made sense, the lack of bird song or wildlife, humans had killed this area for every man and beast, part of our great industrial revolution in the Victorian era that had come back to haunt us.

Ron took us back in the fading light through the woods towards our stinky cottage; as we walked he started to tell us of the old days at the mine, of children working 14 hours a day for little more than a meal - and of the power hungry owners who cared little for those who died while digging out their copper riches. Ron had opened up another world and taken us there, mesmerised by his thick accent and deep colourful descriptions of the miners. As we strolled back through the darkening woods, I held the gun for him.... Just in case.

By the time we got back to our cottage it was dark and Ron invited us to a game of darts in the farmhouse. 'You're on, Ron', I laughed as we parted, I knew that I was quite good at darts and the thought of thrashing Ron appealed to me, serve the old dog right for scaring me to death. Later that night we played darts and exchanged stories with Ron and his wife. Ron cracked open a bottle of his best home-made blackberry wine.

'Try this boy, it slips down the throat like the Devil in velvet trousers', and so it did with a burning sensation and a comforting feeling. The dart board was nailed to the back of the kitchen door which was so perforated that I was amazed it was still doing the job that it was made for.

'Where's Tess'? I asked idly during the conversation, expecting the beast to be snug under the kitchen table where all good farm dogs live.

'We does not allow that dawg in 'ere, the dirty beast, she sleeps in the barn does she', replied Ron as if I were stupid to ask.

By midnight I was seeing at least three dart boards and we had been thoroughly beaten by Ron, the sneaky old devil and his wife who were far better dart players than we thought possible. The more wine he drank, the better his aim became until he was throwing darts like a pro; on the other hand, as the intoxicating home made elixir took hold of me, it became clear why there were so many holes in the door frame.

We walked happily back through the muck to our stinky little cottage. I placed the dining room rug under the mattress and folded all our coats above that and slept as peacefully as a babe in arms.

The week passed quickly and we became accustomed to the smell, even the flies seemed to ignore us after a few days. We probably smelt like everything else around the farm. I soon knew the 'ins and outs' of a working Cornish milk farm, how to make the best award winning butter and the complete life cycle of a milking cow, that, in the old days would produce milk for over 20 years. On the last day, after doing everything from ringing the family bells to running for our lives from Ron's prize bull (he was so mean, no one had the guts to put a ring through its nose) we felt sad to leave. It made me realise something very important that has stayed with me to this day. One person can really make the difference between heaven and hell. Ron had changed a place that most people would find appalling, into something very special. He had lived on the farm all his life and taken over from his dad, as his son would take over from him. He worked every day of the year, even Christmas Day, and never complained; from a young lad delivering his dads milk on the cart each day, he had slowly grown into a toothless wise old man with a splendid sense of humour. His favourite saying was a beauty; he would say it to us each night as we left his farm.

*Sleep softly my friends*
*And wake with a smile*
*Death is forever*
*Life's only awhile*

By the time we left, I had forgotten all about my plan to get a refund from the agent and built up a tremendous respect for Ron. I also learnt an important lesson in life, a lesson that would be of benefit to anyone: People might forget what you say, they might forget what you do, but they never, ever forget how you make them feel.

*The great Singer's grave in Devon*

*Eastbourne seafront with the Red Arrows just visible above the pier. They put their spectacular display on for several days in the height of summer*

*The carpet gardens decorated with the lighthouse and a Red Arrow all in plants*

# THERE IS ALWAYS ONE

Ring, ring, went the phone. Should I answer it? Ring, ring, I was half way out of the door ready for my daily rounds. I paused for a second to deliberate; I realised I had made a mistake the second I picked up the phone.

'My machine does not work, I want somebody out here, now', a high-pitched voice squealed down the line. I could not get a word in edgeways. In cases like these I have to find out if it was me that fixed the machine in the first place. More than once I have suffered a tyrannical onslaught only to find that it was another repairman and nothing to do with me. I calmed the woman down and got some particulars out of her.

'Just wait a minute Mrs Brown I just need to get your details out'. It was the same old story; I had heard it several times over the years,

'I have only used my machine once and it has broken again'.

Some cases are genuine but nightmare memories haunt me, of travelling many miles to find a customer had not plugged her machine into the socket, or put the needle in the wrong way. I grabbed her notes and went back to the phone, thinking that I should have gone with my first instinct and left the phone for the answer machine.

I keep notes on all my customers, and very handy they are too. Mrs Brown's notes were a beauty; she was a full-time professional curtain maker who hammers her machine daily. I came back to the phone armed with ammunition. I still had to be careful, as some customers, particularly when they are after a free service, could often be really tricky.

'Mrs Brown', I said in a calm voice, ' Do you have more than one machine'?

'Oh no just the one, the one I paid you to repair', she replied in an abrasive manner.

'Well my notes say that we have not called on you for over a year, can that be correct, as you have just said it was repaired a few weeks ago'? I was carefully setting my trap.

'Ah, maybe it was a bit longer than I thought, but nevertheless I have not used the machine and I am certainly not paying to have it repaired again', she replied in a strong assertive voice, as if that would swing the balance back in her favour.

'Well Mrs Brown, I am at a bit of a loss as to what you are saying'. My trap was starting to close; the mouse was sniffing the cheese.

'Whatever can you mean', she replied in that, how dare you imply I am not an angel tone.

'Let me explain Mrs Brown', I said keeping my voice in a calm tone. 'You are a professional curtain maker by trade, are you not'? There was a silence; you could almost hear the creaking of the steel wire as her head entered the trap.

'I do not sew as much as I used to' she spurted back with indignation. But her momentary silence had given her away.

'But surely in over a year you have used your machine more than once'? I answered trying not to let the smile on my face sound smug over the phone. I did not want to lose a customer, even an awkward one.

'I suppose so', she replied in a resigned voice, like a schoolboy caught playing truant. Snap.

'I am happy to repair your machine for you Mrs Brown, but it will be a normal service and repair charge'. I have now adopted my hypnotic snake charmer voice to sooth her into a more pleasant temperament. This works both ways for I am now probably more wound up than she is, and I need to relax.

'Oh well, if I must pay, when can you fit me in'? The game was won. I silently praised the Lord for good records.

It does drive me mad when I get these 'special' customers but they are a necessary part of the business. Some are far sneakier than others, like the ones that spend ages cleaning out every single particle of fluff on their machine so that even a crack forensic team could not find anything. Then I have to make a decision whether to try and make them pay or just put it down to experience. Of course there are the genuine cases where I have really done something wrong, my best running score was 437 repairs without one complaint, then came the phone call.

'Hello Mr Askerpov'. (Can't anyone get my name right?) 'My machine seems to be a little out of order'. She was genuine and her notes say she was just an occasional user, so she probably has not used the machine since I repaired it. I arranged to call on her and found to my surprise that I had not tightened the needle bar screw enough and it had slipped up, thumping through her son's denim jeans. I was more than happy to repair the machine free of charge and all was well. I even went back to one woman after five years and repaired her machine for free, as I knew by the dust that she had not used it. Mind you the problem was that it had seized up through lack of use, so I knew I would be back in another five years to release it again. Luckily, these are few and far between, in a normal working month I would rarely have to revisit a customer.

I was running 30 minutes behind schedule and bolted out of the door like a greyhound after a rabbit. As soon as I hit the traffic on its way into town I could just sit back and relax, I was going nowhere in a hurry for the next few miles. My first call was in St Anne's Road, a road that I had cycled down every day for years on my way to my paper round. All six boys in my family did paper rounds to earn money, pocket money was for other children, every penny we had we had to earn. On one trip down St Anne's Road, in the middle of winter, something happened.

The road is fast, even today with all the main bumps smoothed out; it is a fast, steep hill. From our home in Ashburnham Gardens, it was the first hill we went down. On some winter mornings it was so cold, you could not breathe as you rocketed down the hill. We learnt to take a deep breath at the top and that would get you nearly to the bottom before you had to take another. It was a great hill for kids. I ended up in hospital once after racing with my younger brother, Max, down the hill. I fell off and he landed on top of me, needless to say, he was unhurt, I had to be stitched up. Anyway, I digressed; it was on one such occasion, on a dark winter morning that Max and I were bombing down St Anne's Road at full speed. We did not have our lights on as it was wasting precious battery money. Bike batteries were expensive and were only to keep the police happy, they never lit up the road for us. I remember the countless times we heated up the old batteries to try and get an extra few hours out of the dim lights.

So, we were hurtling down the hill at full speed, when out of Enys Road came a police car. He did not see us. It was pitch black. Max was just in front of me in our daily race and he hit the brakes hard, of course those bike brakes on a cold winter day, are practically useless. Max hit the back of the police car, catapulted over his bike and landed, like a sack of spuds on the roof of the police car. The car screeched to a halt, which was the last thing I needed as I then careered into the car as well. Then P.C. Bacon, that was his real name I am sure, got out of the car, Max slithered down onto the boot. Max like the rest of us was a tough kid and was only winded by his unexpected meeting with the 'plod', however, P.C.Bacon was well on the way to a heart attack. He went bright red, brighter than any of our lights, even with new batteries. He went into a verbal onslaught including hand signals, swore blind we would spend the next 50 years in a high security prison, dragged Max off the car and sped off into the darkness. After he went, we just looked at each other then burst out laughing. We laughed so hard that I had stomach cramps for two days.

High summer was leaving us, slowly and gracefully like a duchess in a silk gown leaving the midnight ball. I knew the cooler days of autumn would soon be bringing the early dew to call on the pastures; mushrooms would peek their white bonnets out of the soil and another season would be here.

I apologized for being late to Mrs Dodds at Butts Cottage, my next call; while her rather rude bull mastiff stuck his nose straight into my groin without so much as a by your leave.
'He seems to like you', she announced after examining the dogs face. 'You are lucky, now we won't have to lock him away, he is very particular about his guests'. Thanks, I thought, so nice to please the dog, I'm sure. We marched upstairs in procession, Mrs Dodds, the dog, followed by the lowest order in line, me. I found a sickly Pfaff in the bedroom, ailing from over oiling from her farmer husband who thought anything mechanical would benefit from a pint or two of best engine oil.

I spent an hour cleaning up the machine under the watchful eye of the bull mastiff that stared unblinking, straight back at me with a menacing look; it knew it could have me for a snack anytime. I was glad to hit the road to my next customer and left the mutt pacing the driveway like a well-trained guard.

I visit many cottages, houses and roads with the name 'Butts' in. When I was younger I always wondered why someone wanted to call his or her dwelling Butts Cottage or Butts House. Eventually a customer who had changed the name of his cottage from Rose cottage back to Butts cottage told me what it was all about. It was a reference to an old law past by the Crown that every town and village must have an area to train archers, in case of war. These places were called 'Butts', which were the large bails of straw that they used for the targets. It was decreed in the reign of Queen

Elizabeth I around 1570 that every market town must have a place of practise - 'The Butts'. English archers were the first and best line of defence; also attack. And no archer in the land was better than the farmer who had powerful muscles from working the land all day. People were amazed when Henry V111's flagship, The Mary Rose, was lifted from her watery resting place, that the bows on board ship had a 180lb pull, some 60lbs stronger than experts thought possible to pull in battle. The strength that an archer from the olden times must have had in his arms to pull a bow of that power was awesome, no wonder the arrows could pierce full body armour at a hundred paces. It was the very unpopular King Richard III, who outlawed our much loved game of football and decreed archery must be practiced every week. King Richard, who allegedly was involved in the disappearance of the princes in the tower, only had a short reign. He was the last English King to be killed in battle and no sooner was he gone than football came back.

The English bowmen were the scourge of the French and it was from this mutual hatred that one of our most English of gestures came; the two-fingered salute. Churchill used the famous two-fingered salute during the 1940's, as a sign for victory, when rallying the troops on his many moral boosting tours. But it was the English bowmen who first used it centuries before. The reason for this was, if an English bowman was caught by the French, they would symbolically chop off the two fingers with which he pulled the string on his bow. During the many battles that the English and French had, the English bowmen would wave their two fingers at the French, showing them they still had them and were going to use them to fire their arrows. I wonder how many football hooligans of today have the slightest notion where this most English of gestures originated from, while they are waving their fingers at the opposition.

Paul, at Arndale Upholstery, near Heathfield, was waiting for me as I arrived. I was delivering his Brother industrial overlock machine that he had been waiting for. With Paul's help I quickly unloaded, set up the machine and demonstrated its abilities. The first time I met Paul, many moons ago we were much younger men and I was called out by his partner Angie to fix a rotten overlock machine; the machine was nothing but trouble and ended up being thrown away. I walked into his workshop as

Paul was just tacking down the edge of a leather chair. He had a row of steel tacks in his mouth and looked like Hannibal Lector on a bad day. With superb skill that only comes from years at the same trade, the magnetic tipped hammer came up to his mouth, a nail attached itself to the head of the hammer with a faint click, then the hammer was brought down onto the edge of the leather being tacked to the chair. This amazing feat repeated itself at an incredible speed, tick-bang, tick-bang, tick-bang, until every tack from his mouth had gone and the leather was completely tacked down onto the chair. There was no need to ask Paul how long he had been in the upholstery profession; I was watching a master at his craft.

I left Paul playing with his newest acquisition and headed north to a factory in Wadhurst. Wadhurst is set on the edge of the East Sussex countryside near the Kent border. It was not far from here that the notorious highwayman Dick Turpin made his most famous hold-up on his trusty steed, Black Bess; though once again historian and storytellers are at odds as to who the real rider was; movie makers have favoured Dick Turpin. Turpin was by all accounts a mean and malicious man; I suppose just the right character for a highwayman. The early 18th century was a hard and turbulent time in England. Press gangs roamed the streets, forcibly throwing men into 'His Majesty's Navy' to fight the Spanish. It was a time of master and servant, with little in between. It was growing up with this backdrop that turned Dick Turpin to robbery.

At around four in the morning, at Gads Hill in Kent, Dick Turpin spurred Black Bess into action; he stood astride Bess on the main highway, pointed his musket at the stagecoach and shouted to the driver those famous words, 'Your money or your life'. After the hold-up Turpin made the ride that led him into the history books. With his stash from the robbery, he rode non-stop from Gads Hill to York.

Turpin and Black Bess undertook the amazing ride of 250 miles in less than 15 hours; Turpin made it to York by six in the afternoon and rested in a local tavern, making sure many people saw him drinking. When Turpin was caught and tried, his alibi was simple but effective; no one could be in two places at one time. In court, Turpin was picked out by the stagecoach driver as the highwayman but the ride from Kent to York was thought impossible in such a short time. Turpin was set free to rob again. Dick Turpin carried on with a spree of horse theft and cattle rustling. A clumsy and violent man, he even shot one of his accomplices dead in a bodged robbery. Eventually he was caught and hung for his crimes in 1739. His body left to rot on the Gibbet. Morbidly, they used to call the way the hanged men danced as they died on the gallows at Tyburn, The Tyburn Jig. Many a highwayman ended his days dancing the Tyburn Jig.

After a quick repair at the Wadhurst factory, and a normal service on an old Frister, I was just leaving Mrs Marshall's house when I spotted a broomstick behind the front door.

'What is the broom stick behind the door for'? I enquired casually as I walked out into the porch.

'Oh that is for a full moon, when I do a circuit of the town with my little cat'. We both looked at the black cat sleeping on the mat, at peace with the world.

'Ah, I see', I replied, actually seeing nothing at all. Was Molly Marshall telling me she was a witch? Or was she having a laugh, she was completely straight faced, no hint of a smile. I left pondering, what on earth was that all about? I meet a lot of funny old dears like that almost every week. I often wonder where they all come from, they must have been normal when they were younger, perhaps it was all the beef they ate. Anyway they keep me in business so I never complain, actually they make my job much more enjoyable.

I drove off to my next call at the convent. It had been a while since my last visit and today was a special occasion. Sister Mary was having her old Singer 201K converted from a treadle to electric, she had developed arthritis in her knees and the treadle had become painful to operate. The convent had put some money away for her as a present. Mary had reached her Golden Jubilee; 50 years in a closed convent and that was something to celebrate; they all had a' whip round' and collected enough to have the conversion done. I arrived up the long winding path to the old converted manor remembering how funny it was the last time I called, when Sister Magdalene had come to visit me for no apparent reason, zimmer frame and all.

No sooner had I rung the doorbell than an old nun ushered me in. I walked slowly behind her as we went down the long silent corridor to the main hall. As I walked into the room I was confronted by paintings on the far wall of the sombre nuns in their habits. I remembered them instantly, a more mournful row of paintings would be hard to find anywhere in the world. I glanced along the row of hard faced nuns as I walked towards the Singer at the end of the room. To my astonishment I recognized the last painting, it was an oil painting of Sister Magdalene. She was looking down at me over her glasses with a wry grin, the artist had even put her hearing aids in; it was as if I was looking straight at her. After a row of sorrowful nuns, to find Sister Madeleine at the end sniggering was almost too much to bear. I burst out laughing. In the quietness of the manor, I sounded like a foghorn going off. I had to put my hand over my mouth. I coughed loudly as Sister Mary shuffled over to me.

'Sorry about that sister, I must have had something in my throat'.

'Yes, she had that effect on me the first time I saw the painting', Sister Mary replied smiling.

Sister Mary was in an upbeat mood, gifts do not come often to a closed convent, and in their small-enclosed world this was a big event. I spent some time converting the treadle and left Sister Mary happily buzzing along with her new motor. As I came out of the drive I stopped and pinched a big apple that was dangling temptingly off a low branch in the orchard. I felt like Adam in the Garden of Eden, biting the first apple, but boy it tasted good; a sharp crisp sweetness that only a perfect, in season apple has when it is allowed to ripen on the branch. I guess the world had already fallen apart, so one more apple should not make too much difference. As a child I was always scrumping apples, from neighbours trees, creeping into their gardens when no one was around and enjoying their forbidden fruit, I was like a mischievous little monkey.

I wound my way down towards Battle for my last call of the morning at The Old Forge, a converted blacksmith's forge that had been made into a beautiful Sussex cottage, the sort of place that should be serving afternoon cream teas. I was assisted by a very serious five year old who needed to know every name of every tool and every piece of the sewing machine. I thought that he would soon give up but half an hour later I was still explaining all the parts of the sewing machine; this was much to his grandparents delight as they sneaked off and left me with the young Einstein.

Talking over a cup of well-needed coffee I happened to mention that their sewing machine, a pretty Singer, was fast becoming collectable, with this Mrs Bonner sparked up that she used to have a really old American sewing machine from her grandmother. When I asked what had happened to it she told me it had been left in the garden shed for years. My ears pricked up, was this, a chance of adding a machine to my collection.

'Have you still got the machine now'? I asked hopefully.

'Well, sort of, oh yes it was a Howe, that's right I remember it well, it had a brass picture with his head on it. You see, when we decided to get rid of it we could not be bothered to take it to the tip'. At this point I was eagerly nodding to prompt her not to stop, I was as keen as my dog waiting by the door for her walk.

'Then', she continued, 'I am afraid to say we dug a hole in the bottom of the garden and buried it, I could point out the spot if you like, you are welcome to have a dig around for it'.

Typical, just typical, the one good find I come across all year and it had been buried. I left her house toying with the idea of returning with a metal detector but I knew from experience sewing machines do not like being buried in the damp English soil. I have a machine that was found on a farm near Lewes, that had to be sandblasted and although it looks all right, it is nothing special and will never have real collectors value.

I headed back towards Eastbourne with thoughts of the rusting Howe being dug up by some member of an archaeology team in a thousand years and pondering on its owner. What a grand story I could tell him of how it got there.

Back in Eastbourne the heat of late summer was pouring onto the holidaymakers that were still taking late breaks. In the evening after a long day I leaned against the porch at the front of the house with a cup of tea and thought about my customers, how the day had started so badly and ended up so well. The warm bricks of the house felt good against my shoulder. I looked up to see a flock of seagulls heading back towards the coast, silent white specks against a pale evening sky; they would spend the night floating on a watery bed, safe at sea. There was a hint of coolness in the evening air, I knew it would not be long before the shades of autumn were on us again and the cool nights to come would make my toes sneak back under the duvet.

*The soft South Downs unique and beautiful, no place on earth looks like the Down's. Watching the seasons change in the area is a great privilege*

*Out and about at another summer event. This was a military show and great fun, I really wanted to drive the truck I was leaning on but the owner would not let me*

# HEATHER'S STORY

What a great start to the day, an easy ride through the East Sussex countryside to the port of Newhaven, some eleven miles from Eastbourne.

When I was just knee-high to a grasshopper my dad had a boat at Newhaven called 'La Otre', French for 'The Other' which was an excellent name for the boat as he spent a lot of time there. At weekends 'us kids', mainly my next elder brother, Nick, and I would spend many hours whiling away the time, fishing from the jetty or doodling around the harbour; while dad and often his friend, Sparky, would spend their time resting and having a few drinks, you know, it was a sort of man thing to do after a hard weeks work. It was on one such weekend that something really funny happened; at the time I could have been no more than eight or nine and I caught my first really big fish, to me it was a monster and unforgettable.

Sparky was my dad's friend's nickname, as he was a naval radio operator during the war. Sparky always made me chuckle; he had an easy smile and a great howling laugh. Over the years I had watched his rambling beard turn grey and his teeth fall out, one by one. In the end he had two teeth precariously dangling in the front of his mouth and looked like the typical old sea dog. He always took the time to talk to me and I appreciated that. One weekend Sparky and dad were well into a drinking session on board 'ship' and were at the happy stage of inebriation that many a sailor enjoys. I was alone and relegated to fishing on the jetty for little minnows. I had a small fibreglass rod that was the top end of an old broken rod, which had been pushed into a piece of wood as a handle. On the end was a piece of line, no reel, just a hook. It was no more than two foot long. I had dug up some river worms on the side of the bank and was happily dilly-dallying on the jetty, my toes dipping into the water and daydreaming like little kids do. Suddenly something huge grabbed my bait. I could not hold the beast; I had hooked some sort of monster from the deep. I screamed to dad for help but he was oblivious to my cries. In true fisherman form I was not going to let go of my rod, I was hanging on for dear life, fighting the beast. Eventually, Sparky looked, bleary eyed, out the back of the boat to see what all the commotion was about. He saw the little rod bent over double and the line swishing around in the water.

'By God he has something big on the end', He shouted to my dad.
They both lurched drunkenly out of the back of the boat and stumbled onto the jetty. Sparky grabbed my rod and my dad got down onto his hands and knees to try and grab the line. Between the two drunks it was a comical scene. There was a lot of shouting and waving of arms and eventually they heaved a huge eel onto the jetty. It slithered and writhed about like a possessed demon. Dad wobbled back to the boat and emerged with a wooden pole to beat the brains out of the eel. Unfortunately he whacked Sparky straight over the knuckles. This was followed by a lot of sea faring profanities that gushed from Sparky's mouth as easy as water from a spring. Eventually dad smacked the eel a good blow to the head and it flopped stationary on the jetty.

'By God that's a big'un', Sparky said, as we all stood over the eel examining it. 'There's enough for the whole family there. Well-done boy, now let's get the hook out'. Sparky lent over the eel and tried to get the hook out but it was stuck fast.

'I'll chop its head off', announced Sparky in his inebriated tone, out came the big filleting knife. Dad and Sparky were standing rather unsteadily on the jetty and Sparky proceeded to chop the eel's head off. Dad knelt down and held the eel with a cloth while Sparky chopped its head off. As Sparky reached down the eel's mouth to remove the hook, the severed head bit down onto Sparky's finger. Sparky leapt up and ran up the jetty with the beast's head still gripping his finger, my dad in wobbly pursuit, waving the wooden pole. The whole scene was so funny that I could not stand, I had fallen to my knees and was close to wetting myself watching the old sea dog dance up the jetty howling to the sky profanities that no child should have heard. Eventually after several more slaps with the pole, the two drunken sailors returned arm in arm, patted me on the back and took their trophy down into the hold to celebrate over. I was left on the jetty eagerly trying to catch another monster. It is memories of childhood like that, which make life worth living.

I remembered well, the customer that I was calling on. She had an annoying little girl that followed me everywhere; when it was time to leave she walked all the way down to my car, on the main port road, and then tried to get in. I could not just leave her there, I had visions of her being smuggled off to Greece and sold to gypsies. I had to pack my tools away and walk all the way back to her house, then, while her mother held her, I made a dash for the car.

As I was let in, I asked tentatively where her daughter was. 'Oh she will be down in a minute, she is just getting dressed'. I wondered if I could get the machine fixed and hit the road before the Devil's spawn arrived downstairs. I started the machine in a rush, but ground to halt when I found the problem. It was a broken gear that needed to be stripped out and replaced with a new one. I was about halfway through the job when I heard the stairs creak, too late, I was trapped, l looked up in dismay as the door opened.

'Hello there, remember me'? Came a sweet voice from a blonde haired angel. I stared at the heavenly apparition that floated into the lounge.

'No I can't say that I do', I said in a perplexed tone, expecting to see the horrible little girl, 'have we met before'?

'Silly, it was me that tried to climb into your car all those years ago when I was a kid'. It was the same girl but the difference was unbelievable.

'You have changed a bit since we last met, have you been taking growing pills'? I laughed.

'Its funny what a few years can do to a girl', she replied smiling, 'but you look the same, with a few added grey hairs I notice', she said examining me.

'That's my mature old man look, it is all the stress of having to deal with troublesome little urchins, like you were'.

'Well it suits you', she said with a grin, wafting past into the kitchen.

Wow, what a change, and all for the better, mind you she must be a right handful for her mum, still that was not my problem; I finished off the machine and bade farewell to the family. When I got to the car I turned and looked back, just for a second, wondering if she would appear, as she had done all those years ago. Needless to say, she did not.

At the back of Newhaven, huge machines were cutting into the Downland chalk and dropping it into lorries, they were using the chalk for foundations of a new housing estate. To me it was sacrilege, the destruction of beautiful Downland for even more houses in our already busy corner of England. The Downland was never going to be replaced; it had taken a millennia to produce the chalk that was once living sea creatures; then the seabed had been pushed up by unimaginable pressures emanating from the centre of the Earth into the majestic, unique hills that we now have. Once the chalk was removed, it was gone forever, a sad and depressing sight all in the name of progress. Unfortunately, hindsight only comes after the event, never before. That is probably why visionaries are so rare, people that can guide a nation and its people with ideas of the future. A visionary would have palpitations watching the hillside being removed, and I was none too pleased either; some council official would have told his committee how important it was and how necessary it was to use the chalk that was just lying there doing nothing. It makes my blood boil. Luckily, for every person that destroys, there is one more that tries to protect, so the decline is slow.

I put the thoughts of my beloved Downland destruction behind me and headed for my next call to Hailsham. Hailsham is a thriving market town that was mentioned in the Doomsday book in 1086, but has even earlier Saxon roots. Famous for Burfield's, the rope makers that have made rope for two centuries; Burfield's have made all kinds of rope from ropes for great cruise ships to the old hangman's ropes with 13 turns above the noose. Today Hailsham still retains much of its charm, with a main shopping street surrounded by ample parking and old buildings from many different periods, pubs, shops and bakeries; the centre of town is dominated by the superb, square spired 15th century Norman church of St Mary's; built on the site of an old Saxon meeting place. The spaces around the edges of the town now used for car parking, was where the animals would have been stored for market day, which was held down the main street each week. They used to block both ends of the street and have stalls along the entire length for animals and market produce. Today, there is still a market on the edge of town and the place was, as usual, humming. Whilst developers have tried to ruin the town it has somehow, against all odds, kept its charm intact.

I was calling on an old customer, Heather, that always liked to tell me of the 'old days'. Heather had been born in Bodle Street, some half a dozen miles from Hailsham, in the same house that her mother had been born in and her mother before that. There was a tradition in her family to return home to have the baby. In Bodle Street there is still a little cottage with two bedrooms that once belonged to the Croft family. Her grandmother, Mrs Croft, had 13 children in the cottage. It would be hard to imagine the squeeze in such a small place. Heather's mum used to say that at bedtime the kids were just stacked against the wall for the night. Heather's grandfather, 'Granddad Croft' was a well digger, a man in great demand. For every house that could afford a well would have one built. He was a hard but well respected man in the area. Heather described him, 'as a man of few words but stout heart'.

'Hello, sweet pea', Heather said as she saw me walking along the corridor laden with all my tools like a horse bound for market. She had been waiting outside the door of her little one-room apartment, in her old people's home. It was always a pleasure to see her smiling face.
'Fancy a nice bacon buttie before you start'?
I melted at the thought, but my mouth was open and the words spilled out, 'No, no, no, no.... yes please'. Oh, how little resistance I had, but boy, a bacon buttie with a mug of hot tea, I think even a priest would give up a new convert for one.

Heather had jammed her mum's old Singer 99K that her mum had bought new in 1916. Heather's mum was 'thrown into service', as she put it, at the age of 14; she had been sent to work in Brighton in a large house as a chambermaid. It was a heart tugging wrench from the family home, full of her brothers and sisters and, being unable to get home, she only saw her family once a year, Christmas. While Heather's mother was a maid she saved every penny she could and within two years she had enough money to buy a brand new sewing machine. It was a grand day, the day she carried her new Singer back to her bedsit flat in the top eaves above her Brighton workplace. Heather would never part with her mum's machine; the little piece of metal and wood holds a thousand memories, like the wedding coat her mum made. Unable to afford the material for a nice dress she made a simple but pretty coat from woollen blankets and decorated it with spring flowers.

By the time Heather entered the world her dad had already lost a lung in The Great War, being gassed in the trenches by mustard gas. It did not stop him lying about his medical condition and signing up to fight again in 1939. Once again he survived, being on the last fishing boat out of Dunkirk before the Germans captured it. Luck had been with him twice, but he did not push it a third time and retired to a quieter life in The Home Guard. However, that streak of independence was in Heather as well as her father.

At the age of 15 she enrolled in the armed forces. They never questioned her age; they never questioned anyone's age who looked old enough to fight for their country. Heather's mum and dad knew she had enlisted, but they also knew that she would not be stopped. However, there was a get-out clause that many a family used. Most parents knew their children were enrolling to fight and whilst the government were happy to have as many volunteers, compared to conscripts, as possible, they also turned a blind eye to checking their age. But, if you wanted out of the forces, that was a different matter. You had to buy yourself out and that was very costly indeed; they did not like the idea of training you so that you could just go home when you felt like it. Heather's mum and dad hatched a cunning plan. As Heather was under age, she was not legally allowed in the forces, so if Heather hated it, she was to get a message to her dad who was going to march into his local police station and demand his daughter's return. All this was unnecessary as Heather loved helping with the war effort and married her wartime hero, Percy.

I always adored a trip to Heather's, she seemed to jam her mum's machine on a regular basis, though to be fair she did sew for the whole of her rest home and used her machine daily.

By late morning, with that comfortable feeling in my belly that you only get from bad, bad food I was off to Thimble-Inas, a craft shop in Bexhill High Street. Norman had collected another group of machines for me to work my way through. In his basement under the shop I spent the next few hours drinking coffee and ploughing away at the machines one after the other. It is an exhausting job because you have to concentrate completely on what you are doing; one error, one mistake and Norman would have a complaining customer, and nobody ever wants a complaining customer, nothing can boil the blood like one of those.

As the last machine case was placed on it's machine, I sighed a deep sigh, time to head for home and a break. The late days of summer always feel special, like a bonus of sorts. Deep in the back of my mind I knew that any day the weather would change, cold winds would rush over from Scandinavia and Poland and heavy rain clouds would refill the half empty reservoirs. I drove back along the Ninfield Road towards Eastbourne; I had taken the longer but far more scenic route, as I knew I had a few hours spare. The corn was high in the fields and yellow daisies and dandelions blazed a sunny trail along the roadside verges. The road meandered in front of me like a drunken sailor along a cobbled street. Combine harvesters were busy rumbling away in the fields making hay while the sun shone. It was a hot, lazy, hazy summer afternoon; on days like these no man or beast moved fast, it was as if we all knew rushing would get us nowhere. I looked up at the great pylons that strode across the Hooe Road carrying electricity to distant towns, giants amongst the corn. Swallows were chatting on the telephone wires outside the Red Lion in Hooe and I knew inside locals would be doing the same as they had done for centuries over their country fayre and cold ale. The week had flown by, Friday afternoon had come as fast as Monday morning had disappeared. I was almost finished for the week and looking forward to a nice evening walk on the Downs with Rolly. As I drove towards home I could not help smiling at the thought of Grandma Croft stacking up her 13 children for the night.

*Each step that you take on the Downs opens another glorious image of the downland*

This is a really interesting picture, the whole of the country had a terrible day weatherwise. Eastbourne basked in sunshine all day. You can clearly see the clouds all around but they left Eastbourne alone. One of the reasons Eastbourne often wins the sunniest place in the country, they say that the Downs affect the clouds.

*Eastbourne in full swing with Chitty Chitty Bang Bang making a star appearance*

# Everyone has a Story

Most people I meet have a story; I have become convinced over the years that almost everybody has one. It does not matter how boring it may seem to the individual, eventually it becomes interesting to someone like me. I adore tales from the old country girls of village life; now these stories of working the land all day and lighting-up gas lamps at night, reading stories by the side of the fire, to me, are wonderful, nostalgic and timeless. Now for the bad part, for every story that I remember and manage to write down, I must listen to a dozen others; some are not so interesting and some are fascinating. I desperately try to remember them, often to no avail; I rush home, crank-up the computer, but the page stays blank. One old sailor I met in Peacehaven last year told me several wonderful tales, full of excitement and colour; I got home and could not remember the half of them.

Jim was an old sailor, a salty sea dog of the first order. Even outside his bungalow, an old anchor lay in the garden and seashells were thrown amongst the flowerbeds. He had worked aboard many a ship and tramp steamer in his life at sea; he had been shipwrecked off Borneo and sunk in the Atlantic, a man of many tales. However, he also had an old sailor's smile that you can never trust. So his tales may have been true or maybe not, I certainly was unable to tell. In the midst of his tales came once again, the sewing machine.

One of his jobs was to repair the sails on board. The ship's sewing machine was called 'the sail maker's donkey'. Jim used it almost daily to sew-up anything from a ripped sail to the cook's pants. The sea was in his blood; his dad was also a sailor. Jim told me that the first time he saw his dad walking up the road in his white sailor's uniform with his sack slung over his shoulder, he knew he was going to be a sailor as well. Even Jim's bungalow had a tale to tell. His dad had won the plot in a raffle during the Great War.

The part of the Downs that is now known as Peacehaven was formerly referred to as New Anzacs because of all the Australian and New Zealand troops stationed and barracked there. In 1914 a businessman, Charles Neville, bought thousands of acres of open Downland, then split it all up into building lots and tried to sell it off. To begin with the building lots did not sell very well, what with a war going on, so he thought up a clever plan. The plan was to hold a huge raffle amongst the servicemen; the lucky winners would get a plot of land on which to build their dream home after the war had ended. It worked like a charm, thousands bought into the raffle hoping to win one of the plots of land and Jim's dad, along with many hundreds of other servicemen did win one.

However, there was a snag, the Great War ended and many men never came back. They say that many of the plots of land were taken by people who claimed they had won, but never actually did. That was all well and good as long as no one ever turned up with a winning ticket claiming the land at a later date. To this day, insurance companies, have special clauses in them around the Peacehaven area to cover them against a relative producing one of these tickets and claiming someone's property. Mind you the massive development of housing, all laid out in a very sprawling, boring manner does nothing to enhance the town, it was once know as 'Bungaloid Hell', in recent years the council have done much to improve Peacehaven and the benefit is clear to see.

Jim had called me out because he had dropped his sewing machine onto the hard tiled floor and it had cracked like an egg. The sea dog was not one to give up, undeterred by the calamity; he had the machine welded back together. That is when he needed some expert help to reset all the timing points on the machine. How many people would ever consider welding a broken machine together, it spoke volumes about Jim, he could probably survive quite happily on half the money I earn and still get fat. Mind you, he could tell a tale. By the time I left him I was convinced he could place his hand on the bible and swear to me that I had four legs and a tail.

My next customer also had a seafaring tale to tell and although I had called on Sylvia many times it was only when I enquired about an old photo on the wall that her fascinating story came to life.

Sylvia's father was a Navy man. He had run away from home and enlisted in The Royal Navy at the tender age of 13. However his military record did not start until his 19th birthday. I suppose it was a way of protecting him from signing up underage. George Nesbitt had the luck of the devil in his early life. He started at the lowest position on board ship, as an engine stoker. By the time he retired he had stripes on his arm and was saluted by the crew. George was born the year before Queen Victoria departed this earth, 1900. By the time he was 40 he had served in one war and was well into another. He was on board the ill-fated HMS Hood, the flagship of the British Navy. The Hood was the best-equipped, fast ship in her class, capable of over 30 knots. To work on the Hood was the best job in the Navy. George had married Elsie who was ten years younger than him in the 1930's; it was Elsie's machine that I was fixing for Sylvia to use. Elsie fell pregnant in 1940 and George arranged for compassionate leave to be with Elsie after Sylvia was born, it was this leave that saved his life, for in May of 1941 The Hood came up against her arch rival, The Bismark.

The German Bismark was a formidable war machine, a huge mass of floating metal and weapons. The guns of the Bismark were more powerful than that of the Hood and had a far greater range. As the two ships came together in the Denmark Straights the outcome was never in doubt. The huge Bismark cannon pounded shell after shell into the Hood's side. The attack was short and violent, in less than eleven minutes the Hood suffered a huge explosion, probably in the armaments hold. The 860ft giant listed and went to her watery grave in less than 180 seconds, taking 1400 of her crew with her. It was a terrible slaughter and a shock to the nation in her darkest hour. The one good thing to come out of the carnage was that George was safe and sound, holding his baby daughter on compassionate leave.

In 1941 George bought his wife a surprise birthday present, a new sewing machine, a Singer 66k. He paid 23 pounds and 13 shillings for it, complete with the cabinet, three months wages. I know that because the machine still has the original receipt. It was a surprise birthday present that Elsie never forgot. On her birthday all she had was a card. Times were hard, the war was raging all around them, so she did not expect anymore than a card. Inside there was a surprise, the receipt for a sewing machine. As she was reading it, trying to comprehend what George had done, there was a knock on the door; outside was her new machine, she cried for an hour.

I know today that the thought of a sewing machine as a birthday present probably does not sound too brilliant, but in the 1940's it was every girl's dream, to be able to make her own garments. There was just not the choice there is today and if you did see something that you liked then you probably could not afford it anyway. George had to wait six months to get the machine. This was because the Singer factory was busy churning out machine guns and bullets, as many as twenty million bullets a week. Luckily, the Singer was actually made just before the outbreak of the war, and simply finished off the next year. If he had tried to buy one in 1943 he would have had to wait several years before Singers got back into serious sewing machine production again.

It was amazing to hear Sylvia tell of her father's lucky escapes throughout his life. Sylvia said, George was born lucky, and he knew it, George once told her, 'Fate may have laid down my destiny lass, but not the path I take to it'.

*The beautiful carpet gardens. Yana's family looked after the gardens for 70 years from around 1900.*

*The Polegate windmill just down the road from us. Every villager would have eaten bread with the grain ground from her, now she is a silent reminder of our past.*

This is a sweet poem of how I would imagine a perfect harvest day from long ago on one of the many old farms I often visit.

# Windmill sails
## *By Alex I. Askaroff*

*Windmill sails cuffing the harvest air,*
*Heavy horse resting without a care.*
*Grain a grinding, husks gently falling,*
*Sweat on Father's brow, skylark calling.*
*Late morning breeze scented with flowers,*
*Working the land all daylight hours.*

*Field mice scatter from Dad's scything blade,*
*Mum's setting out our lunch in the shade.*
*Yeasty fresh bread and lumps of ripe cheese,*
*Buffered scones with honey from our bees,*
*Swifts swooping, soaring, darting, diving,*
*Fields of golden brown, country thriving.*

*I'm just soaking up this harvest day,*
*Too young to help, I'll be in the way.*
*While Dad is busy gathering straw,*
*Chasing field mice is my only chore.*
*Dilly and dallying all day long,*
*Humming a tune or singing a song.*

*Patches on my shorts, mud on my face,*
*Hair in tangles all over the place.*
*Cornflowers swaying beneath a blue sky,*
*The moist warm earth, Mum's blackberry pie.*
*Dad silently eating, time rolls on,*
*And all to soon our paradise gone.*

*Windmill sails cutting the harvest air,*
*Heavy horse resting without a care.*
*Grain a grinding, husks gently falling.*
*Sweat on Father's brow, skylark calling.*
*That summer day safe in memory.*
*With Mum, Dad and their little imp - me.*

# THE EMERALD RING

'Good morning Mrs Cornford', I called out as she opened the gate to Highland Farm and I drove in.

'Thought you were the vet', she answered, 'we have a sick ram in the paddock needing some expert help, he has torn a bit of his underbelly on some barbed wire'.

'Well nothing I can do about that I am afraid, is it serious'?

'Oh no, Billy has had much worse than that over the years. Ah! Here he is now'. The vet, in a new four-wheel drive Daihatsu, followed me in; he got out in a lovely clean tweed jacket and pulled on some sparkling Hunter wellies.

'Looks like a new boy on the job', I whispered to Sally Cornford as she closed the gate.

'Well, we shall see what he's made of in a moment', she replied as she waved the vet over.

I started work on her tatty old Singer 447 in the barn as she and the vet walked down to the paddock where Billy was waiting. I could see through the barn door that Billy was not a happy sheep. He was jumping up and down against the metal bars, where they had him penned in and was making a nasty, squeally-neighing noise, like a cross between a sheep and a pig. Rather him than me I thought as I got down to work on the mucky old machine. The Singer had been used to make everything from horse blankets to tea towels and had had a hard life. Still, no sooner than it was cleaned and oiled, and a few minor parts replaced, she was up and purring like a newborn kitten.

I looked out of the barn as I was cleaning up and saw the Cornford's all circled around the new vet in the pen. I walked down the farm, passing the old shed with chickens scratching the farmyard floor for a few grains of corn thrown out earlier by Sally, passed the sheep dogs that gave me a lazy glance and down to the pen. At the pen the vet was in a right state, he had taken off his lovely tweed jacket and placed it over the top rail of the pen, rolled up his sleeves and got down to business. The jacket was the only clean piece of clothing that was left, the rest of him looked as if he had been in a mud bath. His lovely pristine Hunter wellies had more mud and muck inside them than out. His spotless check shirt was splattered and smeared with the same stuff that was lying prolifically over the floor; the vet himself was bright red and losing the fight with the boisterous patient.

'I can see the problem', I said to Sally with a knowing nod, pointing to a terrible swelling between the ram's legs.
'Silly bugger, that's his assets, the gash is further up his belly'.
'Oh, now you know why I am not a vet', I replied gazing in embarrassed astonishment at the ram's huge assets that were swinging freely between his legs. Sally saw my expression, which showed quite clearly that I had never seen a breeding ram in his prime.
'Billy will service my whole flock in less than three days when I need him. He is at his peek at the moment'.
'I can see', I replied

It was amazing how mesmerizing it was watching a vet at his work. We all leant on the pen in various positions and watched the poor young vet eventually get the better of Billy, mind you that was only after he administered something that made the ram pass out. He carried on regardless of his muddy condition making sure the ram was clean and safe. The gash, which was about two inches long, was cleaned, shaved and stitched in a neat little row.
'Bet your sewing machine could have done that' Sally's husband called across the pen.
Before long the ram was brought round. He was let out of the pen and raced out of the yard into the field, not a happy animal by the look of it. He stopped in the field some twenty yards away and shook his head; suddenly, he turned and raced back toward the vet. The poor young vet leapt out of the pen, knocking his clean jacket into the muck. He need not have bothered for at the last second, Billy darted off sideways and ran back out to the pasture. The vet cleaned up as best as he could with the hose that was attached to the end of the barn. He scraped as much muck as he was able, off his lovely jacket and put all his equipment back in the Daihatsu before making a quick escape out of the farm.
'Well that's a lesson he has learnt today', Sally said watching the car disappear, 'Fancy him turning up here, tuckered up like a lord at a party to work in our farmyard. He won't be doing that again in a hurry, he has been

watchin' too much telly, it ain't all like it seems on the box, he will be shaking muck out of his boots for a week and if he thinks we are paying for his dry cleaning when he sends his bill, he's got another thing coming, a good slap from me'.

I left the Cornford's laughing at their poor new vet, I could not help feeling for him; he had done a good job with little help from them. He was not going to get an easy ride from the Sussex farmers who spend their lives scraping a living from the soil; still we all have to learn, he will find that they will give him respect once he has earnt it. I could just see the Cornford's down at their local pub all having a good laugh, performing the tale of their new vet leaping over the pen and knocking his last bit of clean clothing, his tweed jacket, into the muck.

The soft morning had left patches of mist in the valleys as I drove to my next call at The Brown Bread Pony Sanctuary in Brown Bread Lane, Ashburnham. The countryside looked like a faint watercolour painting that should be hung on an art gallery wall with hedgerows and trees lifting out of the mist like forgotten forests. The villages looked as if they were set in some lost landscaped from a 1950's musical. Shafts of light were dropping down onto the road through the trees like the inside of a dark church on a bright day. The lanes down to the sanctuary, where the sunlight was catching them were steaming like a Turkish bath; even this late in the autumn there was some good heat in the sun. I had made my way down Bodle Street and Windmill Hill along Tilly Lane to the sanctuary. Views of the landscapes hidden by the dense growth of the hedgerows suddenly opened out. Green fields with sheep grazing in the mist with the warm sun on their backs looked magical, it lifted my heart sand filled me full of vigour for the day ahead.

The leather machine at the sanctuary had been 'repaired' by a friend and returned to them in a non-functioning condition. All I had to do now was get it working. I had heard that story many a time; the friends are just being helpful but soon get out of their depth and drop the machine off worse than when they found it. I am then left trying to sort out what they had done and get the machine working properly.

The sanctuary was full of ponies and horses in various conditions, some of them had been left and unloved, some had just become too much for their owners to look after; all of them had found a new home at the sanctuary where they would find happiness. Horses, besides dogs are probably the closest animals to man on this planet. There is an attachment that people make with horses that is stronger than blood ties. Many times a horse has been listed in divorce proceedings as being shown more love than the husband, quite often rightly so.

They also have brilliant memories. I remember once when I was a kid; my dad was picking up some eggs from a farmer out near Cowbeech. At the back of the farm was a large paddock where two horses lived. One Sunday morning while dad was busy putting the world to rights with the farmer, I decided to go for a ride. The horse had no idea what I had planned, he was not even aware that I was racing down the field as fast as my little legs could carry me; his first notion that I existed was when my hands slapped his rump as I leap-frogged onto his back. I made a perfect jump and landed like John Wayne, smack in the middle of the horse. I grabbed his mane and hung on. The horse had other ideas; he was not carrying passengers today. He leapt and bucked and in an instant threw me straight over his head, somersaulting onto the ground. I landed dazed and looked round, to my dismay the horse had decided that I needed a lesson in manners. Far from the grass chewing, pretty horse he had been only seconds before, it had transformed and charged at me like a crazed monster. I leapt to my feet and ran for my life with the snarling beast close on my tail. Of course my brothers, who were watching on the safe side of the fence found all this most amusing, shouting encouragement to the horse. I almost cleared the fence in a single bound as the horse slid to a halt, neighing with all the strength he could muster. He stood on the other side of the fence, hoofing the soil and snorting at me, his eyes rolled back and wild.

In all the years that we visited the farm the horse never forgave me. If it caught a glimpse of me he would throw a tantrum, running at the fence then rearing up and scraping the air with his hoofs; and that's how I know horses have a good memory.

It was an easy job getting the machine at the sanctuary working, the needle bar timing was out and soon it was ploughing through the backlog of horse blankets and rugs that were so desperately needed with winter fast approaching.

I was soon at Mrs Patford's in Ninfield to repair her Great Aunt's machine that had not worked for over half a century. She had dragged it out of the attic to repair some net curtains that had frayed at the edges.

'I am not saying a word Mr Ashkerof, I have just bought your book and I do not want to be featured in your next one'.

'Ah but you might like being in it', I laughed back. 'I could describe you as a beautiful princess or a rich countess'.

'No thank you I have said too much already, I am now going to get you a cup of coffee, white with two sugars I believe'.

'Blimey, you really have read the book, yes please', I answered with a big smile on my face. That was a draw back I had never thought of, no one will talk to me in case they end up in one of my stories. Perhaps I should use a non de plume, or whatever they call it, yes, my next book could be something like, Tales from the East by Raphael Doublepoint, or Mutterings from Afar by Mustnot Talkalot, how about, Fruity Stories by Victoria Plum.

I was well amused by the time the lady of the house returned and it showed on my face.

'And why are you so pleased with yourself, may I ask'? She said handing me the coffee.

'Ah, that's because I know something that you don't', I replied.

'And what may that be'?

'That you are going to be in my next book'

'Why'?

'Because of this', I said handing the lady something that made her stop dead in her tracks.

In the machine, near the needle bar I had found a superb and precious diamond and emerald 18-carat gold ring.

'I have pulled many an object out of a sewing machine before but never something quite so valuable', I said to her as she slumped dumbstruck down into a chair. I could see tears welling up in her eyes and put my coffee down.

'What is it' I asked, gently.

'This ring was my great aunt's. As a child I had always loved this ring and played with it when we visited her in her old mansion down by Bexhill seafront. Now it all makes sense, of course it does, after all these years, I simply cannot believe it'. She stared at the ring holding it up to the light

and watching the diamonds sparkle and the emeralds gleam with their green lustre.

'You will have to tell me now'. I pleaded. 'You can't leave me hanging on like this, what are you talking about, please, please tell me, I have to know. By now she had composed herself a little and started her story.

'When I was still just a small girl, my parents and I used to visit my Great Aunt at the end of every month. We would meet with some of the other family, other aunts and uncles, that sort of thing. She had an old butler, Wilfred was his name; he would bring afternoon tea for us. Strange old man, Wilfred, always looked like he was about to fall over, sort of stooped and bent, he used to scare me. He wore a coat with long black tails like an overgrown swallow's tail. If it was sunny we would sit out on the veranda overlooking the seashore, it was wonderful'.

'While we were all having tea, my great aunt would usually send for me. I would be taken to her bedroom, it was very posh and Victorian; I can remember it as if I was there yesterday. She was so grand and well, almost spiritual. She always dressed in black and had beautiful soft white hair tied above her head, like a great round loaf of bread. On her left hand she always wore this beautiful diamond and emerald ring', she said holding it up towards me.

'It was the only ring she wore besides her wedding ring. One afternoon she told me that she was going to leave me a strange gift and that although I would not appreciate it now, one day I would understand, I had no idea what she was talking about, I could have been no more than 9 or 10. Anyway I soon forgot all about it and chatted away with her, sometimes we would talk all afternoon, forgetting all about the other relatives in the drawing room. I would tell her all about what I did at school and what the family were doing. While we talked, or more like, I talked, she would always brush my hair in front of this huge dressing table mirror, with a lovely silver hairbrush. I used to sit on a stool with her behind me; she would let me play with her ring, this ring, while she delicately brushed my hair. I used to let my hair grow really long so that it would take longer to brush. I used to love the way she would take such care over it, I felt like a little princess. On this occasion, when it was time to go, she told me to make sure that I always kept what she was going to leave me and never sell it. I promised, kissed her and skipped back to my parents who were happily idling away the afternoon with Wilfred standing in the corner of the room, hovering like an old bat'.

'I left her that day still not understanding what she meant; she died three weeks later. I cried for days; my mother told me that I cried enough to fill a village pond. At her funeral I was really surprised how many people came and how many relatives she suddenly had, they were never around when she was alive. At the get-together afterwards, all I could hear people talking about was how much money did they think she had, and who was going to get it; I had to go in another room and cry, no one seemed sorry that she was gone except me. I so longed for her to be there and brush my hair for me, just to be with her one more time to tell her I loved her. I had my hair cut short after she died and never grew it long again'.

Sometime later, I can't remember how long after Aunt Aggie died, my mother brought me this sewing machine, the one you see here, and told me that my great aunt had left it to me, she had no idea why and nor did I, until today. It was Aunt Aggie's way of giving me this beautiful ring that I had always loved, without the rest of her family pinching it, God bless her soul'.

At this point she started to cry again but they were tears of joy, tears of a lost childhood being found, of a distant memory, a light being rekindled in the darkness.

Well, if that is not a most beautiful story I don't know what is, I won't put it in my new book if you do not want me to', I said to her as she wiped her face with her hanky. I had thought about offering her my handkerchief, but it was a paper one that had been in my pocket for days and not quite suitable.
'Oh do put the story in, I would love to read it and remember my dear aunt one more time'.
'You've got it', I said, 'Oh, and of course without the ring jamming the machine, your Singer is making a perfect stitch, so now every time you use it you can remember her'.
I left my customer playing with her machine, staring at her gold ring and stroking her hair all at the same time, she did not know what to do first. That was one happy lady. Strange how we humans can cry with laughter, happiness mixed with sadness all at the same time.

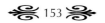

At my next call I put my foot in it with my usual delicacy. I was talking to the lady of the house and she kept interrupting me. That is not unusual and I am more than happy for it to happen. Now, the husband was in the other room listening to his wife interrupt me all the time. He suddenly piped up 'let the man finish will you'.

'He always butts in, my old man, just ignore him', she whispered.

'Well', I said. 'Little piggy's have big ears'.

She looked at me and burst out laughing. 'Not that funny', I thought, until she pointed to the photos on the wall of her husband all dressed up in his police uniform. Oh God, I had done it again, dropped myself straight in the mire, completely self-inflicted, as usual.

'Oop's' I am so sorry', I said quietly.

'Oh, don't be, it's the best laugh I have had all day'. At this point her husband, all six foot six of him entered the room to see what all the fuss was about. I put my head down and carried on working, looking very serious at the internal workings of her Brother machine.

'What's all the noise about then'? He asked quizzically.

'Oh nothing dear just something I heard on the Jimmy Young Show, on the radio, that made me laugh'. I kept my head down but felt the full force of his stare bore through me. I knew if I looked up I would see him staring straight at me, so I kept my head down.

I was glad to get out of the house before the wife let it slip what I had said. Calling a policeman a pig even by mistake is not too smart even by my standard. I had visions of a size 12 boot up my backside, helping me out of the house.

I made my way down to Cooden for one last call before lunch then headed along the old coast road to Pevensey Bay. On the little beach huts that lay along the first part of the beach as you leave Cooden, starlings were gathering on the rooftops in their hundreds. Above them swallows lined the telephone wires and in the fields on the other side of the railway lines, groups of goldfinch were lifting then dropping into the bushes, like washing blowing on a line. They were all on their last stop on British soil, waiting for a favourable wind before shooting the sixty miles across the Channel. The little huts the starlings had perched on were no more than six feet by eight and where many a happy childhood was spent on the

beach. Miles of open sand at low tide and fresh air are what summer holidays by the sea are all about.

This part of the coastline is one of the last unspoilt parts of our area, how long before the developers come-a-calling is anybodies guess. Miles of open pasture and farmland with panoramic views must be so tempting for developers. For now, it is still a blissful part of old England, unchanged for decades.

I stopped at the Normans Bay railway crossing, the last manually operated crossing in the country and waited for the Bexhill train. Before long the gentle hissing of the rails announced the 12.30 to Bexhill. It raced passed with a loud hoot, a shaking and a buffeting wind; the lineman appeared from his small hut and opened the gate, waving me through, I waved as I passed and he touched his cap. He is like the last lighthouse keeper, a dying breed. It won't be long before he is replaced by an automated system of blinking lights and clicking solenoids. It is sad, but as inevitable as one breath follows the next.

I made my way along the old road to the back of Pevensey Bay, passed my old home where I spent many a happy hour at number 266 Coast Road. My dad had a bungalow right on the seafront and our back garden was the sea. I spent two happy years there, fishing and walking along the miles of open sand with him. At night I would let the sound of the waves rock me into blissful sleep and the fresh, salty smell of heaven would greet me each new day. To this day, I have never slept so well as I did by the sea.

It had been a busy morning, what with mistaking a ram's impressive 'assets', for a swollen wound, then dropping myself in it with a huge policeman. However, the real joy of the day, was the expression on the face of a lady when she saw something that had been lost to her for over 50 years; that gold, emerald and diamond ring had whisked her away on a journey through time, to visit a long forgotten aunt and her strange butler in their seaside home, to feel once more like a little princess.

*Yet another satisfied customer.*

# EPILOGUE

'I can't be absolutely sure Archie, but I think your feed cam has slipped out'. I had my sleeves rolled up and my arm half way up-a huge Singers 32's innards. I could feel the feed cam slot but could not get my arm round far enough to relocate the bearing. As much as I twisted and shoved, the brute would not move. I stopped and laid the machine back on its bed. As I straightened up my back ached from the stretching. Archie looked on in silence and tapped his pipe on his boot. 'How did it happen Archie? I have not seen this fault on one of these before'.

'Twas that there', Archie said, pointing with his pipe to a large heavy riding harness. 'I was on the last length too, 'nother few seconds it would have been finished. Now I got a customer that's complaining and an I suppose a bill from you to boot'.

'You know me Archie, if I don't fix it, you don't pay me'.

'Suppose its wurth it', he muttered, cocking his head to one side at the thought of having to lay out hard earned cash.

Archie was one of those people that you had to get to know before he would even give you the time of day, they say in his village pub that he is so mean he would not give you the dribble off of his nose on a cold day in Hell. I had always got on with Archie but, I suppose, I had a grudging respect for a man that could survive off the land and do well from it. In his barn, where I was working, every time we went quiet, I could hear scratching behind the corrugated sheets. Archie would bang the sheets with his foot and cough. I suspected rats and kept a sharp look out for the little devils. I was even more convinced when I saw Archie check the pellets in his air rifle. I would not put it past Archie to be having one of the critters for his supper. The last time I called he was roasting a pigeon that he had shot off his roof. 'Teach 'im to keep me awake', Archie explained as he saw me staring. I have eaten wild wood pigeon and it does taste good. Mind you, I draw the line at rats.

After another struggle with the Singer beast I managed to get my fingers around the bearing and simultaneously slip the locating rod back into position. I stood up and heaved a large sigh.

'Lucky all machines are not as big as this brute', I said to Archie who was busy rubbing an oily cloth over his rifle. Archie just murmured something out of the side of his pipe and carried on rubbing away. He probably thought I had just put a show on for him. I wiped away the grease off of my arms, rolled down my sleeves and packed my tools away, no point asking Archie for soap and water, he would just give me a look as if I were mad. Every time I visited Archie's place I itched afterward. I nearly always had to have a shower as soon as I got home; there was definitely something living in the sacking around his barn that liked me.

As we walked out of the barn the brilliant autumn sunshine dazzled me and I squinted looking for the back of my Land Rover. Archie rummaged around in his baggy pockets and pulled just enough money out to make me happy and him choke; he handed the crumpled notes to me one by one, straightening them as he ceremonially placed them in the palm of my hand. 'Month's wages that', he said.

'It might have been a month's wages a hundred years ago Archie but what with fuel costs and all....'

'Spare me the speeches', Archie interrupted, then turned and walked inside the barn, kicking the door closed with his old boot. I knew he would be in a mood for a week over having to pay for his machine, but I also knew he was a wealthy man. Although Archie made his living off the land he failed to mention to anyone that he owned several farms in the area and sent his children to private schools, however, he still used old string for a belt.

I drove through the old village of Ripe making my way back to the main Eastbourne road. I passed The White House, where I had spent many a happy hour fishing at 'Uncle Robert's'. Uncle Robert was not a real uncle, but you know what it is like when you are a kid and keep asking who a person is, 'He's your Uncle now that's an end to it'. He and his wife Agatha were really just good family friends. Robert was an old Polish pilot who had retired to a Sussex smallholding and worked the land, Agatha was a typical English country lady with snow white hair, tied in a bun behind her small head and a wonderful, soft and perfect upper class accent; she was always surrounded by her beloved cats, I once counted 16 in her kitchen, lazing around by the wood burning stove. The cottage was on the site of an old quarry that had been filled in to make a wonderful lake. Over the years it swarmed with thousands of small fish and some large carp that crept through the murky silent depths, occasionally surfacing with noisy gulps as they sucked down air and floating debris. As keen fisherman we always tried to catch these monsters of the deep but invariably ended up with small rudd or roach. However on one fishing trip we caught a monster.

I had been fishing quietly under some branches, away from the other boys who were happily catching rudd on small reed floats and tiny hooks. I noticed a large swirl by some of the branches of an old willow whose branch tips dropped into the lake like children's feet dipping into the water. I sat and watched; sure enough it came up again, a large carp. I got my little rod and hooked a small flake of bread crust onto the hook, when the fish dropped down I cast over the branches and let the crust float temptingly above the carp's head. Sure enough the big lazy carp rose to the surface and sucked the bread straight down. Suddenly the peace surrounding the lake was shattered as the lazy beast turned into a wild monster. My brothers all came running as they heard the commotion. They found me with one hand trying to hold up my shorts and the other hanging onto the rod. With a little help we managed to drag the golden carp ashore. We stood gazing down at the largest carp I had ever seen; it must have weighed seven pounds at least. Compared to the tiny rudd we had been catching, this was a prize beyond all description. It was too large for the keep-net and knowing little about which fish could be eaten we decided to take it home for supper; Mumsie was bound to be delighted, or so we thought. We wrapped the monster in a wet towel, packed up our tackle and crept around the side of the cottage so Uncle Robert did not catch us leaving; he would have not taken too kindly to us pinching his prize carp; we grabbed our bikes and high-tailed it back to Eastbourne. It was a long ride, about seven miles and the fish was heavy, weighing down my paper-round delivery bag in which we kept everything, occasionally even papers. I knew all the effort would be worth it once we got our prize home.

Back at Ashburnham Gardens we unrolled the carp and found to our amazement the beast was still alive. So we quickly filled up the bath with fresh water and plonked the carp into it. We stood over it, watching it slowly recover in the clear bath water, within a few minutes it was swimming up and down as if it had lived there all it's life. We waited patiently for Mumsie to return from the factory so we could show her supper. When she did return, she was not quite as enthusiastic as we hoped. She stared in horror at the monster swimming around in her bath; it had turned the crystal clear water to a muddy brown. After some energetic persuasion she agreed to cook the carp for us, but not before it was clean. So each morning before I went to school I would empty the bath water and fill it up with fresh, each night when I came home it was muddy again. This went on for a week, no one had a bath, to the six boys in the household, this was no big deal, Mumsie, on the other hand was far from amused. After about a week the water slowly started to stay clear. Each day when I returned the carp would look at me and swim aimlessly around its little enamel tank, I looked on at the helpless captive, knowing its days were numbered. But something happened, much like a hostage and kidnapper syndrome, we all wanted to let it live, we even gave it a name and talked to it. When the big fish kettle came out of the cupboard we had to think of a cunning plan... and fast.

No sooner was Mumsie's back was turned, than we wrapped the carp up again and fled on our bikes down to our local park. Motcombe Park is a beautiful small park where the River Bourne springs to life and where Eastbourne gets its name. In the park is a nice size, clear pond full of small sticklebacks no more than an inch or so in length. We clambered over the rails and let the carp slip into its new home. I am sure the carp must have thought it had died and gone to heaven. It looked supreme amongst the tiny fish as it glided around the pond. We went home happy that our pet had survived and was in a place where we could see it every day as we passed on our way to school. Mumsie was not too upset, as she had the feeling it was not going to taste much good anyway. But the story does not finish there. Such a large fish appearing from nowhere caused a mass of local gossip and it became quite an attraction for several weeks. We dare not say anything for fear of reprisals; but would often bring breadcrumbs in our short school trouser pockets and watch for it to appear from under the weeds. It caused quite a stir in its day. What we used to get up to, I don't know. We used to have so much fun, always getting up to some sort of mischief. Like the time our new 'posh' neighbours moved in.

The Metcalfes were a very polite and impressive couple who moved into the house opposite us in Ashburnham Gardens, Christopher was later to be awarded an Order of the British Empire (OBE) for his outstanding work;

that was of no consequence to us, they were bait. We spied on them through the curtains and thought we had better introduce ourselves. My younger brother, Sam and I hatched a plan. We stole a pig's trotter out of the fridge that Mumsie was going to boil up for our supper- she certainly knew how to spoil us!! We brushed all the mud off our school blazers, I then slipped the trotter up my sleeve; in front of the hall mirror, at a glance, we both looked quite presentable. Sam and I walked across the road and knocked on the Metcalfe's door. A pretty, middle-aged woman with a soft Swiss accent answered the door. We later found out she was Peggy Metcalfe. Sam was in front of me and said in his best possible voice, 'My name is Simon', (We just shortened it to Sam, with six boys in the family you have not got time for whole names), 'I live opposite you at No7' he continued. He then held his hand out to Peggy, 'Pleased to meet you I am sure'.

Peggy took his hand and shook it firmly.

'.... and this is my brother Alex', he said, moving to one side to introduce me. I also said in my best 'toffee' voice, 'One is pleased to meet you too', I held up my arm and extended the pig's trotter, Peggy, calmly reached out and took hold of it. I shook it wildly, she looked down at the cold, clammy thing that she had grasped and screamed, we bolted back across the road in fits of laughter.

My God, we got up to terrible things when I think back on it. We were certainly the scourges of our area, when the Askaroff boys were out, nobody was safe.

On the way home from Archie's I took the back roads past Arlington reservoir. Shades of autumn were spreading across the land. The harvest festivals had all come and gone, the village flower shows and vegetable contests had all been judged and the allotments cleared for winter planting. The harvesting machines had all been packed away in barns and farm buildings for another year. The close-cropped fields looked empty and bare, like spiky haired punk rockers with a harvest gold rinse. The squirrels had packed their food away for the winter and the lambs' coats were becoming thick and warm for the cold months ahead. Before long the first frosts would come to call and spread a white sheet across the gentle Downland.

The storm of the previous night had left the countryside looking a shambles, like a house after a children's party. Leaves and small branches were everywhere; unripe chestnuts torn from their wooden limbs lay scattered along the verges. There was also freshness, a cleanness; crystal clear, striking views of the downs and farmland unhindered by the summer haze, the wet road was a shining brilliant reflection of the bright day, almost too bright to see. Some council workers were clearing the drains of the mud and rubble that had washed down the road during the night. One of the workers had a shaven head except for one tuft of peacock blue hair in the front; he smiled as he saw my expression. Most British, even the young ones' are slightly barmy.

I pulled over off the main road and stopped in the small priory car park just below the Long Man at Wilmington, my silent giant friend that safeguarded the countryside and downland lay against his soft grass bed opposite the car park. How wonderful the area looked, show me a view of Sussex in autumn and I will show you a view of heaven that makes your heart sing. It was late afternoon and the end of another busy week of phone calls and emergency repairs, of complaining old men and fascinating stories. I had travelled many miles and worked many hours, but enjoyed every second. How different to the days at the family firm, the constant pressure and hard grinding work with little pleasure. I had left all that behind, as a fading memory, I had leapt out on my own and carved a new future.

I sat and let my eyes wander over the majestic views; I pondered on how I would never have known all those years ago how my life would turn out. I had seen the seasons of the year unfold over Sussex. The Great Storm of 1987 when 15 million trees were up rooted and the floods of 2000 when hundreds of homes and businesses had been affected. Then there were the early days of struggle and hardship, when slowly but surely I lost almost everything that I had spent years acquiring at he family business. The days when we went hungry and I looked at Yana and wondered what we were doing, when even the broken washing machine supplied a glass bowl (part of the front door of the machine) that we used to put salad into. We had kids to feed and a mortgage to pay. Every day was another challenge as I set off in my old van to scrape a living from the area. I had thrown everything I knew away and gambled on a dream.

Although I had not realised it at the time, I had a very vital ingredient in my quest, true friends. Just as, when I was a child, I took my first steps and was encouraged, and when I rode my first bike, I fell off many times, but each time I was helped back on and tried again. My life had been much like that, the help from friends made the impossible seem possible and even when I failed they were there to help me try again. No one should ever underestimate the power of good friends, people that are there for you when you need them most, in your darkest hour.

For some reason, in later life we find failure intolerable, if we fail at something it is all too easy to give up and put it down to experience. As children we never gave up. Supposing you fell over as child and decided that from then on that walking was a bad idea. Life is not about success it is about ignoring failure, few people get things right first time, whether it is trying to walk or their first driving test, it is all about getting back up after you fail and trying again. I had done just that; I made the leap into the darkness and survived. As the months had drifted into years, financial security came and the children grew; I looked forward to every new day and the challenges it held. I had put my heart and soul into being master of my own destiny and it had worked....

# *The End*

*The pretty Motcombe garden with Motcombe Manor in the background. This is the small lake where we let our carp go. Neptune sits proudly on the lake, someone has pinched his trident once again.*

*This old yew at Wilmington Church is well over 1,000 years old. Ancient legends have it that the mighty yew helps the souls travel to heaven, yew trees are often found in graveyards*

*The Long Man of Wilmington at rest overlooking the Downs*

# FAVOURITE SAYINGS

I am always amused, not quite as much as our dear departed Queen Victoria, but nonetheless amused, at what some people say about their machines. Below is a list of the most common ones that have kept repeating themselves over the years.

My husband has fixed it, all the extra bits are in the bag.

I only gave it a drop or two of oil; I have no idea where that puddle came from.

Since my husband kindly rewired it I keep getting shocks, I am sure he is not trying to kill me.

It sews, but don't touch it or you will get a shock.

I thought good quality cooking oil would be fine to use; it was seized anyway.

Doesn't olive oil dry to a nice varnish after a while?

It works, but for God sake don't touch anything metal while your feet are on the ground.

I was sure I had put all the wires back in the same place; still a few shocks won't kill you. (Typical old dear who can survive anything).

It works fine, except it is going backwards.

My husband switches it on and off at the plug and I sew as fast as I can. (This is when the machine won't stop because of an electrical short).

It stitches perfectly on paper, it just does not sew fabric. (Very useful, I'm sure).

Everything works except the stitch.

I never knew computer sewing machines were allergic to oil, can't we just wipe it all off and see if it works again. (This is after her machine has had a meltdown).

I just kept fiddling with it until it all came apart.

It was working until it broke. (Doesn't everything).

Who would believe something so simple would break. (This is the condescending person who has no idea about anything).

There cannot be too much wrong. It is only a sewing machine. (Same type of woman).

Well, it is all going round so there can't be too much wrong with it.

It is probably just the needle. (My most common statement before I have to spend an hour fixing the machine).

The machine is fine; it just does not work.

It was seized, but since I have taken all these parts off it, it is working fine, except the stitch of course.

I have been sewing for 40 years don't tell me which way the needle goes. If I say it goes this way then the machine had better get used to it. (The arrogant sewer who drives me mad).

There can't be much wrong it has not been used since the war.

I promise I never touched it, the bits all came off on their own.

The needle can't be in the wrong way; I never change it.

It was working perfectly until I dropped it.

My husband is an engineer; he has fixed it. All you have to do is get it sewing.

It broke doing horse rugs, perhaps they were a bit heavy for it. (This is always from the woman who has bought the cheapest plastic machine).

Who would have thought a sewing machine would need servicing. (This is always from the old dears).

I lent it to a friend and it never worked again. (Common one that one).

It can't be the needle I only changed it last year.

I only dropped it the once.

They do not bounce too well, do they?

It just exploded but I am sure it is nothing much.

It was the children, they broke it; they break everything. (The frustrated mother).

It was the dog not me, the dog I tell you. (The woman is in denial; she probably does not even have a dog).

I told my husband not to touch it, but you know men (I hear this almost daily).

He just had to touch it; it is a man thing, still he kept all the bits for you.

Who would believe a bit of rust could do that? (This is after the machine has fallen apart after being left in the shed for 10 years).

It is just the tension, just the tension I tell you.

I have not used it since you were last here. (Common one this, then I pull out enough fluff to plant a row of potatoes in).

It has not worked since you fixed it. (That does not surprise me because I have never seen the machine before.)

Don't tell me I have threaded it wrong. It is my machine.

There is no power! Really madam, I find plugging the machine in helps.

# GLOSSARY

| | |
|---|---|
| Allotment | Cultivated land |
| Barrow boys | Market traders |
| Bite the dust | To die |
| Bodge | To bungle/to work badly |
| Booty | Valuable items |
| Boozer | Public House (Pub) |
| BT | British Telecom |
| Chumping | Eating with speed |
| Conkers | Horse Chestnuts |
| Cuppa | Cup of tea |
| Doodlebug | German Rocket Bomb |
| Daft Hap'orth | Idiot |
| Dollop | Lump |
| Fag | Cigarette |
| Fiver | Five English Pounds |
| Frock | Dress |
| Gold Top | Full cream milk |
| Grockle | Holidaymaker |
| Ham-fisted | Awkward |
| Heinz 57 | Mongrel cross breed |
| Hostelry | Pub and eating house |
| Hubby | Husband |
| Hun | German soldier |
| Kip | Short sleep |
| Knee high to a grasshopper | Very young, very small |
| Lav | Toilet |
| Lavvy | Toilet |
| Loo | Toilet |
| Moggie | Cat |
| Moons ago | Years ago |
| Never never | Hire purchase |
| Nineteen to the dozen | Fast talking |
| Palaver | Fuss |
| Parlour | Lounge |

| | |
|---|---|
| Pinnie | Apron |
| Plod | Policeman |
| Pop-his-clogs | To die |
| Posh | Elegant |
| Pushing up the daisies | Dead and buried |
| Quid | One English Pound |
| Rag and bone man | Junk dealer |
| Scallywag | Child up to no good |
| Settle up | Pay for services |
| Sidle off | Sneak away |
| Skin-flint | Tight with money |
| Skip | Rubbish container |
| Slobbering | To dribble |
| Slunk | Creeping in/out |
| Smitten | Fallen for someone |
| Snuck | Crept along |
| Swig | A mouthful of drink |
| Tacky | Cheap and nasty |
| Taking the Mickey | Making fun of someone |
| Tatty | Worn |
| Telly | Television |
| The Smoke | London |
| The Sticks | In the countryside |
| Tickling the ivories | Playing the piano |
| Tipple | Little drink of alcohol |
| Tip | Where rubbish is taken |
| Tipsy | Light headed from alcohol |
| Titbits | Scraps of food |
| Toff | Upper class gentleman |
| Toil | To work hard |
| Totter | Street trader |
| Twitten | Small alley |
| Veg | Vegetables |
| Wellies | Wellington boots |
| Whip round | Collection towards a present |
| Yarn | Old tale |

# FIDDLERS GREEN

*Continued*

## Chapter 4

This is another excerpt from my book, Fiddlers Green, The Village Fayre. It is all about the goings on in a fictional village in East Sussex, leading up to the summer fayre. The book is just a simple tale of village folk and is about half finished. I am introducing all the characters that eventually come together for the fayre.

The kitchen hung in a haze of icing sugar, like an old loft caught in sunlight; trays of sweets were everywhere, truffles and fudges, trays of toffees and chocolates. Teresa's eyes were open wide and she was almost leering at the wonderful selection before her.

'May I'? Teresa said leaning over the tray of chocolate truffles expectantly.

'Oh go on then, you naughty girl', replied Peggy, 'just the one'.

'I have no idea how you two stay so thin', Teresa said. 'You both eat more sweets than the whole village put together'.

'Well, nor do we, mind you we both have terrible teeth', said Peggy.

'We have more canals than Venice', quipped Chloe with a smile.

Teresa bit into the truffle and let out a muffled sigh of delight, both the sisters smiled, they knew just how good their sweets were, they had been making them for over 40 years.

'Now what can we do for you my dear'? Asked Peggy whilst patting a sieve full of icing sugar over a tray of chocolate swirls.

The icing fell, catching the morning sun in sparkles as if in a spotlight, the chocolate swirls the star performers. All three women stared mesmerised by the scene.

Teresa broke the silence. 'I was wondering if, at the fayre today, you could do me a small favour'? She started.

'Go on my dear', Peggy said as if to prompt her. 'You have our undivided attention'. Both sisters knew that it must be something important to bring her here this early. 'You are keeping us in suspense', Chloe chipped in, whilst running her finger round a bowl of rum truffle mix and licking it with an air of satisfaction.

'Well, I have a special visitor today, and I was hoping that you two could show him a good time this afternoon, while I am busy with the judging, you know just keep him amused for a couple of hours'.

'Who is he'? Both sisters said in a wave of excitement and then giggled at the timing of their words.

'He is... he is', Teresa said stammering.

'Come on out with it girl', Peggy said with the air of an impatient schoolteacher.

'He is my brother', Teresa said.

The sisters stopped in their tracks, the kitchen that had been a hive of activity a second before was silent. 'Your brother'! The sisters said again in unison.

'But you do not have a brother', Peggy said.

'I do, but we have not seen each other since we were separated as children and he has picked today to visit me'.

Teresa went on to explain how as children, after their mother's death, they were separated and sent too different foster homes. She had tried for many years to track him down and had eventually given up. Then out of the blue a few days ago a telephone call came and she knew who it was immediately. It was her brother Alistair who had been searching for 40 years and had never given up hope. Recent developments in government policy had released documents that had always been kept secret. It had allowed Alistair to track his sister down and today he was arriving from Birmingham.

' We shall be delighted to look after him, we can tell him all about you', said Peggy with a mischievous smile.

'Not too much I hope', Teresa said. ' I will be with him for a few hours before the fayre and then I will bring him to you on your stand about 1.30 if that is OK'?

'That will be fine, we shall make him most welcome', Chloe said.

'I do like the idea of having a man all to ourselves for a few hours', Peggy said with a wicked grin. 'We shall have all the village gossiping'.

Teresa left the cottage with a bag paper bag full of assorted goodies and a toffee in her mouth. She turned at the gate and waved back to the sisters that were standing in the doorway dusted in icing sugar, both grinning from ear to ear as if they were planning something, which they were. They looked like naughty little schoolgirls that had found a frog on their way to school and were going to put it into teacher's desk.

'What a lovely pair', thought Teresa, oblivious to the chaos that was to follow. She headed off back toward the Green to chase up the school caretaker who was to open all the marquees for the stallholders. She had two hours before her brother was to arrive and a thousand jobs to take care of first. She almost skipped with excitement as she went. 'What a great day it was going to be'.

# Chapter 5

In Tenpenny Wood, the old witch, Mabel Baker was filling the last of her dozen bottles of love potion. She knew that although she was only palm reading at the fayre she would be asked for her special brew. Little did the village realise but many of the locals had been brought together because of her potions, in one way or another. Mabel never asked money for her concoctions, she always exchanged the potion for favours, that way she had most people in debt to her. She was as shrewd as any of her ancestors and one of the most powerful of her whole kindred, learning the way of the witch folk from her earliest years. As the idea of witches became an outdated belief, she had a freedom that many of her ancestral kinsfolk could only dream about. Nobody, well, almost nobody, believed in witches anymore.

 170

She was in an upbeat mood humming away to herself, overlooked by her crows up in the branches. Scruffy, the badger, who was way too wound-up to rest, was following her like a lost sheep as she shuffled around her woodland home. Sleeping by her hut was 'Snortgar', the boar. Known locally as 'The Shagwell Beast', 30 stone of muscle, bone, sinew and fat, a magnificent specimen. He was king of his realm that stretched from the woodlands of Ashburnham right down to the ancient seaport of Rye, in the South East corner of Britain. He was sleeping soundly, dreaming of autumn when the food on the forest floor was most plentiful and life was easy. His back left leg was twitching and scratching the earth as he slept, his heavy breathing shaking the side of Mabel's hut in measured waves of hot hog breath. As Mabel went past Snortgar, he let out the most noisy and foul smelling wind. Mabel kicked the beast and swore at him; he just quivered, licked his snotty snout in a satisfied smirk and fell back to sleep. Snortgar, 'The Shagwell Beast', was in many of the villagers' tales; often told by the old folk around the fireplace at the Fiddlers Arms on cold winter's nights, when tourists were easy prey to a good yarn. In their stories he was a fearsome creature that wandered Tenpenny Woods when the moon was full; he ate small children and other helpless prey. This was far from the lazy, easy going and friendly slob that he really was.

Every now and then as Mabel shuffled around her dwelling she would let out a giggle, reminiscing over all the wicked deeds that she had done through the years. She was a mischievous old witch and today as 'Mystic Mabel' the palmist, she was going to have fun, a lot of fun at the fayre.

Meanwhile, Milly Farthingale, the district nurse, was hammering along Chestnut Lane on the outskirts of the village in her Land Rover. She had just been to freshen the dressings on Emma Harper's sprained wrist. Emma had fallen out of the apple tree the week before, whilst picking apples for her mint jelly, nothing too unusual about that, except Emma was 71. Milly had been the district nurse since finishing nursing college 19 years earlier. She was indispensable to the locals and had delivered most of the children in the village plus a few animals, when Marriott the vet, was out of the area.

Milly was a large girl, reminiscent of a member from the 'seventies Russian shot put team. She had unbounded energy and was known as 'Mad Milly' because of her horrendous driving. Milly took no prisoners when dealing with people; you did it her way or not at all. She was a get up and go nurse and always knew best. She had many a confrontation with Peter, the builder through the years, though secretly she was completely and madly in love with him, as he was with her. In all the years they had known each other they had stumbled and mumbled over their feelings but never dared come out and say it. Milly in fact could talk about anything to anyone except her love for Peter; mind you the whole village was aware that they were in love. They were the perfect couple. At the fayre last year during the 'Tossing the Hay Bale' competition, Milly, had pushed the struggling farm boys aside, grabbed a pitch fork, stabbed a bail and tossed it over the highest pole; much to the applause of the crowd and the delight of Peter. He nearly burst with pride and admiration for her, almost telling her of his feelings, but gave her a polite hug instead; then went and got drunk on hop rich Sussex Ale in the beer tent.

Most of the village gossiped about Milly and Peter but no one ever did anything. Peter boiled with frustration at his own pathetic attempts to declare himself to Milly. At his home he had even built an extension on the back to house all of Milly's medical gear should she ever move in. Milly on the other hand just sighed when she thought of Peter. She knew that he was the man for her. She was thinking of him as she drove towards home. Perhaps this year at the fayre they would manage to get together. 'I know' thought Milly as she screeched around Potters Bend, gravel flying everywhere, contriving a cunning plan, 'I shall get him drunk and then the silly fool might weaken'. She drove on, dust flying from her wheels as she hurtled past the gates of Foxhound Manor towards the village, a smile growing across her face. 'Today he will be mine'.

# Chapter 6

Foxhound Manor stood upon a slight rise, dominating the surrounding countryside. There were two ways to get to the manor, through the main gates that opened onto the Shagwell Road or the back entrance in Saxon Lane. The gates at the main entrance made an imposing sight to visitors. Two columns 20 feet high rose up from the ground. Perched on each column were giant cormorants with wings outstretched, their heads facing each other, beaks open as if in a frozen scream. Through the iron gates, the long gravel drive curved up to a large forecourt. On either side of the drive were two identical rows of yew trees all trimmed to perfection; standing to attention, like guards at Buckingham Palace. In the centre of the forecourt stood a huge Romanesque fountain, the statues depicted a scene from a gladiator's ring. A gladiator with spear in hand, fought with a lion in a deadly embrace as it tried to devour him. Water sprayed from a central tube lifting almost to the height of the impressive building behind.

Foxhound Manor had been home to the Burleigh family since 1502. The manor had started life as no more than a smallholding, a farm of some 10 acres. However the second son to Godfrey Burleigh, born in 1533, had other ambitions. He was a devious and evil man who had little regard for human life, a gambler and a cheat. By the age of 20, he had already acquired a boat from a crooked card game in a Rye tavern. He had set sail, and pillaged Spanish trading vessels off the coasts of France and Portugal. By the age of 30 he was a rich man with three ships and a growing empire.

A cunning politician, born coincidentally on the same day as Queen Elizabeth. He kept favour with the young Queen, though in truth he thought she would fail as a weak sovereign and kept close contact with her opponents. He used his wealth wisely, buying favours at Court. But also wasted much of his spoils on frivolous extravagances. As his power grew it made him more evil and reckless. Many a man fell before the path of Edmond Burleigh. In the years after his death, he became known as 'the infamous Burleigh'.

Though he wasted much of his illegal gains, he also built Foxhound Manor. By 1569 Foxhound Manor was an impressive estate of over 1000 acres. It held on its land serfs and tied cottages, smallholdings and surrounding villages. Taxes from the land poured into Burleigh estates and they flourished. Elizabeth turned a blind eye to Burleigh's attacks on Spanish vessels and always looked forward to his visits to London. Burleigh, in turn showered the young Queen with gifts. An ugly man he had a sadistic streak that scared many that knew him. Though he had no true friends, the life he led always ensured he was surrounded by a flock of willing fools. In 1589 Burleigh was knighted and given a hereditary peerage, for his part in fighting off The Spanish Armada and 'Favours to the Crown'. Though in truth he never put a foot on one of his ships during the battle, he stayed in port, the coward he had become, for as he aged he feared his own death like few men could.

As old age came upon Edmond Burleigh he became more evil and twisted. He would take great pleasure in throwing serfs off their smallholdings to watch them starve. He tried to become more sophisticated and in the year 1594 commissioned a playwright, one William Shakespeare, to write a play for him. However on seeing the first night's performance he refused to pay poor Will. Stating that he would not endorse such nonsense as he had seen. The play was Romeo & Juliet. To Burleigh the idea of true love was as alien and far-fetched as any idea could be.

In his final year, age and illness had made Burleigh a monster. Plagued by gout and old wounds he wandered around Foxhound Manor like an evil spirit. His life had been full of adventure and excitement and power but was now just endless torment. The servants at the Manor prayed for him to be in a good mood and his pains to ease, hoping they may not have to suffer with him. This was to no avail and he would often scold and beat them.

In the winter of 1597, aged 64, Burleigh was bed ridden and dying. The priest had been summoned from St Mary's Church in the village and had rushed with sacred ointment and a bible to his benefactor. In the master bedroom the fire in the great stone fireplace crackled and spat and licked the walls with tongues of flame like a hungry demon waiting for its feed. At Burleigh's bedside, the priest was kneeling and read from his bible in hushed whispers over the dying Edmond, candle wax dripping onto the floor from the candle in his shaky hand.

Burleigh had summoned physicians from London to heal him. They had filled him full of opium to ease his pain, rubbed goose fat and lavender over his back and were bleeding him with leeches. What they did not know was how to cure Burleigh's burst appendix. He lay writhing between the sheets of his Gothic four-

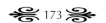

poster bed; the leeches placed over his fat sticky body were sucking more of his lifeblood from him. One physician held him down while another let more blood run from a vein in his neck. It was a horrific scene in the old manor; the sheets were covered in his blood and foul sweat. His screams echoed through the great house right down to the scullery, where Daisy, one of the kitchen staff, sat crying with her hands over her ears.

Burleigh started to hallucinate, and saw the Devil come for him. The Devil waited at the foot of the huge bed, laughing. Burleigh had been a bad soul and the Devil was happy to take him to the fiery furnaces of Hell. He pointed a crooked finger at Burleigh and grinned. Burleigh screamed even more, staring at the edge of the bed in a mad drugged state. The doctors tried hopelessly to control the blood that was dripping everywhere. The house servants looked on at the horror before them and kept making the sign of the cross while praying.

It was as if all of Burleigh's bad deeds had come to punish him this one last time. As the flames from the fire shot shadowy figures around the master bedroom, Burleigh let out one final scream, clutched his throat and died. For a moment there was utter silence. His face, contorted like a hideous monster softened; a final sigh left his lifeless body and it slumped down on the blood soaked sheets. Burleigh's hunting dogs, the only creatures he had ever loved, started baying and howling on the lawns outside the Manor as his evil spirit passed from the World.

Since the death of the most infamous Burleigh, there had been an unbroken line of male descendants. They had struggled through some bad periods of history but as times changed so did the family. The discovery of huge iron and coal deposits on the Burleigh land brought them untold wealth. Then the manufacture of cannon, pounded into life by the great hammers in the furnaces of Ashburnham, brought yet more wealth and distinction. The Burleigh cannon lined the coasts of England to protect her shores; they were pushed into battle at Waterloo and brought Napoleon to his knees, they thundered around the World, as Britain became master of two thirds of it. They were pushed up the Khyber Pass and across the plains of Africa. The Burleigh cannon had become part of the British Empire, and the Burleigh name moved from infamy to its place amongst the ruling classes.

In more recent years the wealth of the Burleighs was in decline. The current Lord Burleigh had taken over from his father, losing most of the estate's wealth in crippling death duties. Rather than give up and sell Foxhound Manor, Lord Burleigh had taken to earning money from the leisure industry. He arranged 'shoots' for the London set. The gamekeeper on the estate reared pheasant. The London boys would come down in their Mercedes and Aston Martins, shoot all day, kill anything they could, get plastered at the Manor, pack their Purdy shotguns away on the Sunday and disappear back to the City. Two thousand pounds poorer but a brace or two of fine Sussex pheasant to give to their amused wives.

A golf course proved popular in the beautiful grounds as did the trout lakes. Lord Burleigh had accepted the challenge of keeping Foxhound manor with vigour, the only thing he would not do was open the doors of his house to the public. He knew it would bring in welcome revenue but the thought of parading his ancestors to tourists every day was just too much for him.

On the morning of the Summer Fayre Lord Edward Burleigh had just finished breakfast of Scottish smoked kippers and toast. He was taking the long climb past the portraits of his ancestors up to the master bedroom. As he walked he gazed up at his scouring ancestors. Portraits of overweight Burleigh's in a selection of wigs lay silent behind their gilt frames. He stopped at Edmond Burleigh's painting, the first Lord Burleigh stared down at him and a cold shiver ran down his spine. The portrait of Edmond had been relegated to the loft for centuries as more of his terrible deeds came to light. But in recent years his devious ways had become more acceptable and held a morbid fascination to others. Much like that of serial killers such as Jack the Ripper; and so he had been reinstated with the other Burleigh's.

At the master bedroom, Margaret Burleigh, lady of the Manor was putting the final touches to her make-up. An elegant women; at 59 she still rode with the hunt and kept herself busy with country affairs. Running the estate was a full time occupation that she handled with zeal. She sat in front of the beautiful Edwardian dresser, still in her negligee; she looked up at her husband, the 16th Lord of Foxhound Manor.

'Edward, you are going to be late for the fayre,' she said in a perfect English accent; perfected from years at finishing schools.

'Now, now dear, replied Edward, you always panic, we have a good hour before we are due to arrive'.

Edward washed and dressed, putting on his favourite cashmere and silk waistcoat; it was a mustard cashmere front with a cream silk back. Down the front were six brass buttons from his old regiment. As he slipped into his waistcoat he felt like he was saying hello to an old friend, memories of his trip to Charwell's, the Saville Row tailors, came back to him. Three fittings it took to get the waistcoat just right. He had judged his weight by it for 20 years; if it became too tight he would go on a strict diet until the garment felt like a second skin. His wife glanced across at him and saw how pleased he looked with himself, she remarked.

'You can still fit into that old rag then'? She said with a mocking smile.

'Of course my dear, fit as a fiddle', he said patting his stomach in proud recognition.

'If I had my way that would be in the bin', she smirked.

'Over my dead body dear'

'That could be arranged,' She giggled, walking over to him and putting the finishing touches to his bow tie. She gave him a peck on the cheek and a little pat

on the backside.

'Now step on it Edward, we have to move, the summer fayre won't wait, even for the Lord of the Manor'.

In private, they showed each other a love that never rose to the surface of their well-trained exteriors in public life. To many people they seemed a distant almost remote couple; few knew of the deep affection they held for each other.

*To be continued.*

Well, that's it, book two all done and dusted.
Now I must get on with the third of my trilogy.